ALEXANDER VON HUMBOLDT

Self-portrait of Alexander von Humboldt (pencil drawing of 1814)

L. KELLNER

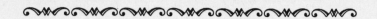

Alexander von Humboldt

LONDON
OXFORD UNIVERSITY PRESS
NEW YORK   TORONTO
1963

Oxford University Press, Amen House, London, E.C.4

GLASGOW NEW YORK TORONTO MELBOURNE WELLINGTON
BOMBAY CALCUTTA MADRAS KARACHI LAHORE DACCA
CAPE TOWN SALISBURY NAIROBI IBADAN ACCRA
KUALA LUMPUR HONG KONG

PRINTED IN GREAT BRITAIN

IN MEMORY OF MY MOTHER

CONTENTS

ILLUSTRATIONS

The frontispiece and illustration No. VII are reproduced from Bruhns's biography of Alexander von Humboldt. Nos. II to V are reproductions of illustrations of Alexander von Humboldt's *Vues des Cordillères et monuments des peuples indigènes de l'Amérique*. No. VI is a section of the map published by Alexander von Humboldt in his book *Examen critique de l'histoire de la géographie du Nouveau Continent, etc.* No. I is reproduced from sketches in Alexander von Humboldt's diary of his American journey, part IV.

The author wishes to acknowledge her indebtedness to the Science Library and the London Library whose treasures enabled her to write the present publication, and to the Berlin State Library and Herr Fritz Lange of the Alexander von Humboldt Committee of the Academy of Sciences at Berlin for the reproduction of the sketches of the Rio Meta, and to the Institut Français in London for the loan of François Gérard, *Correspondance de François Gérard etc.*

INTRODUCTION

ALEXANDER VON HUMBOLDT, scientist, explorer and cosmopolitan man of the world, 'a good European and free mind', was born in Berlin, then the capital of the kingdom of Prussia, on the 14th of September 1769 and died there on the 6th of May 1859. In the course of these ninety years, he explored the Spanish possessions in Central and South America, took part in the scientific life of Paris for nearly a quarter of a century, made an expedition to the Urals and Siberia and served as a chamberlain at the royal court in Berlin without ever hiding his predilections for a more liberal and democratic system. An original mind and a careful observer, he acquired a truly international reputation in an epoch which started with the discovery of oxygen and ended with the commercial production of electro-generators. Cosmopolitan and multilingual, he was pre-eminently a child of the age of enlightenment but also of his country, endowed with the astringent wit of the Berliner. Arago said once of him: 'He has the most malicious tongue of any man I know and the best heart.'

A man of wide talents, he took great pains to develop them as fully as possible; how successful he was, is borne out by the enormous range of results he brought back from his great expedition. He was sufficiently worldly to give the right amount of consideration to the authorities of his time without setting a high value on their rewards. Although he was modest and intelligent enough to acknowledge the merits of greater men, he was not unmindful of his own originality and capable of drawing attention to it since 'blowing one's own trumpet is part of the job'. He was as generous with his own money while he still

B

possessed any as he was with his time in the service of aspiring scientists. His early biographers tried very hard though unsuc׳ cessfully to find a conventional 'love interest' in his life; they ascribed its absence to his complete dedication to his work. His attachment to his brother and his lifelong friendships with other scientists bear witness, however, to the strength of his feelings.

To recall in this period of a new International Geophysical Year the details of his life and his achievements is of timely importance since Humboldt made fundamental contributions to our knowledge of geophysics. He was a master in perceiving the outlines of a general law in a mass of numerical observa׳ tions and equally masterly in the exposition of his material.

One

THE BEGINNING

BARON FRIEDRICH WILHELM KARL HEINRICH
ALEXANDER VON HUMBOLDT was the son of a Prussian
officer and the descendant of a family of provincial administrators. He was born in the Prussia of Frederick the Great, in Berlin, then a rather primitive and provincial town, surrounded by
the sandhills, the pinewoods, the moors and lakes of the Mark
Brandenburg. Mark as the English word 'marches' means a
frontier district, the frontier between the German country and
the Slavs of Eastern Europe. Brandenburg was the core of the
Prussian kingdom which stretched eastwards across the Oder
to include the fertile soil of the former East Prussia with its
capital Königsberg—now Kaliningrad—where the kings were
crowned and where in Humboldt's youth Kant formulated the
Categorical Imperative and deliberated on 'Eternal Peace'.
Northwards, Prussia reached to the mouth of the Oder, and in
the west, its possessions included parts of the Rhineland while
Silesia had been the prize won from the Austrians in three wars.
Brandenburg with its sandy soil and no mineral deposits was a
poor country; its people as in poor countries elsewhere were
frugal in their habits and hard-working. They conquered their
own barren earth by strenuous efforts and the more naturally
endowed of their neighbours by diplomacy or superior military
endurance.

Frederick the Great is nowadays usually portrayed as the
prototype of a despot; in his own time, he did not differ greatly
from the other holders of European thrones, England excepted.
His régime was certainly completely authoritarian; but he was
also an intellectually brilliant man and eminently successful

3

general and politician. And where are now the kings and even more so the presidents of republics who are sufficiently familiar with the Voltaires of our time to quarrel with them? Or where are the Voltaires for that matter?

General education had existed in Prussia since 1717 and was extended by Frederick to the newly acquired province of Western Prussia, his booty in the first Partition of Poland. But, as in France, the peasants were still serfs though they were taught to read and write. The village schools consisted often of just one cold, ill-equipped room, and the schoolmasters, in many cases retired soldiers, were untrained and wretchedly paid. The finances of the state were very straitened after a long period of wars, and as usual, it was found easiest to economize on education.

The privileges of the aristocracy had been greatly strength-ened: most ministerial posts and all army commissions were in the hands of members of the nobility. The king was far from believing in the mysterious qualities of 'blood' but it was his conviction that the aristocratic tradition of service and responsi-bility was the best qualification for public office. It was his aim to achieve a strongly centralized, carefully planned organiza-tion of the country's economic resources, a form of state social-ism in fact. Very few of these plans became reality; the opposi-tion of his own administrators was too much even for his strong will. But he had his way in his agricultural policy. The export of corn depended on a licence which had to be signed by the king; the number of these licences was regulated by the situation of the market and the prospects of the harvest. Private imports were forbidden. At the threat of a shortage of grain, state officials acquired *sub rosa* the necessary amounts on the fairly cheap Polish markets. Speculation in corn prices became thus impossible, and prices could be kept on a stable level. At times of glut, the landed proprietors were relieved of their sur-plus by public purchases at a fair price; at times of shortage, the stores of the public magazines were put on the market to bring the price down sufficiently to prevent widespread famine. The efficacy of this method was amply demonstrated in the hunger years of 1771 and 1772.

Humboldt's father was an officer in the Prussian army; he fought in the Seven Years' War as adjutant to the Duke of Brunswick and became afterwards chamberlain at the court of the brother of Frederick the Great. He had married in 1766 Elizabeth de Colomb, the widow of a Baron Holwede. She was descended from a family of French Huguenots who came originally from Provence and who had settled in a small town in Brandenburg where they founded a plate-glass factory like many other Huguenots. In fact, the German plate-glass industry is still to some extent in the hands of Huguenot families. She was a wealthy woman and was left more possessions by her first husband who had owned Schloss Tegel, about twelve miles north of Berlin and later the family seat of the Humboldts, and Ringenwalde, an estate on the right bank of the Oder. Ringenwalde was Alexander's portion of his inheritance and helped to pay for his expedition and for the publication of his great work on South America.

The rôle played by these French immigrants in the economic and cultural history of Prussia should not be undervalued. They were admitted in large numbers to the country by the Great Elector, Frederick William III. As a counter-measure to the Revocation of the Edict of Nantes, he offered religious freedom, financial subsidies and tax relief to French settlers in his Edict of Potsdam. In the years between 1685 and 1700, about 20,000 refugees entered Prussia and founded French colonies in nearly every town. Berlin had one of the largest; in the thirties of the last century, about a quarter of its population was of partly French descent. It does not seem impossible that the dry French wit and the French ability to look facts in the face has become one of the more potent ingredients of the spirit of the true Berliner.

There were two sons of the marriage, Wilhelm, born in

1767, and Alexander, born in 1769. Their father seems to have been a much warmer personality than their mother but he died suddenly when the children were quite small. Their family life was therefore entirely dominated by their mother's character; she was a very aloof and self-contained woman who provided for their education but gave them no intimacy and warmth. They were expected to show her respect and follow her directions. The children gave the not inconsiderable affection they possessed to each other; they were until Wilhelm's death on terms of the closest friendship, an attachment which Alexander extended to Wilhelm's children. Alexander disliked intensely the cold and constrained atmosphere of his home and once he had left it, paid only duty visits there.

The two boys were privately educated in their town-house in Berlin under the supervision of a tutor. Their first teacher, J. H. Campe, who gave them their grounding in the three R's, became later well known as the translator of *Robinson Crusoe*, a slightly bowdlerized version for the youthful mind, and as an educational reformer in a period of educational reform. His successor, G. J. C. Kunth, who came to his post as a very young man, was their friend and adviser and companion in everything they did. He planned and supervised their studies, rode and swam with them—swimming was then a new and fashionable sport and Lake Tegel was practically on the doorstep of their home—and finally accompanied them to their first university. He remained their lifelong friend and looked after their financial affairs during their long absences from Germany. Through his connections with the Humboldt family he eventually obtained a quite important post in the civil service. This kind of career was not at all unusual at his time; many impecunious young men, very often as in Kunth's case the sons of clergymen, began as tutors to the sons of men of standing and ended up in high administrative posts.

The boys' mother had decided early on that Wilhelm, who from the beginning showed unusual ability, should be trained for a high public office and Alexander for an administrative post in the civil service. He was often ill and did not learn easily. They were given the normal grounding in classics, languages and mathematics and, in preparation for their careers, political history and economics were added to the syllabus. These subjects were taught in what amounted to lec/ ture courses by well/known specialists in the field.

Berlin, the capital of a fairly large kingdom, was at that time nothing more than a country town with unpaved streets where pigs rootled for food in the refuse and street lighting was sparse. The king preferred his Rococo residences in Potsdam, one of which was surprisingly provided with a system of central heat/ ing while the Berliner warmed himself at a tiled stove and froze in icy bedrooms. But Berlin had architectural merits; George Forster who had seen the world, called it one of the most beautiful towns in Europe, a somewhat astonishing statement. The social life of official circles, however, was not very attrac/ tive. Prince Frederick William, the nephew and successor of Frederick the Great, the very antithesis of his uncle, preferred the company of Rosicrucians, alchemists and crystal/gazers to that of French philosophers and scientists. And yet there existed an active intellectual life in the town which owed its existence to a few writers and to emancipated and enlightened members of the Jewish community centred upon Moses Mendelssohn, their acknowledged leader.

The Jewish population of the German countries, as of most other European countries, had no citizen rights; they could not acquire land and were not allowed to learn a craft or enter the professions with the exception of medicine. Trade and business were their only means of livelihood, and they were not free to settle where they wanted. They lived in closed communities and did not even speak the language of the country properly. Any Jew who could read and write German, was considered a traitor by his people. This is a familiar story; not so fam/ iliar is the development of the emancipation of the Jews, an

7

emancipation on two fronts. The Jewish communities had to open their minds to new ideas and a different form of life just as much as their hosts had to overcome their ignorance and prejudices. This emancipation had been started in Berlin by the efforts of one penurious and hunchbacked little Jew from Anhalt-Dessau, Moses Mendelssohn. In 1743, as a boy of fourteen, he had left his home in Anhalt with the burning desire to acquire an education in European thought and know-ledge, a heresy in the eyes of his community. On foot he entered the capital through the only gate through which Jews could pass, and armed with a few introductions tried to find first some means of support since his father was quite unable to give him any financial help. Eventually, he managed to keep himself alive by teaching Hebrew to the sons of the wealthier members of the community while secretly he read German books and taught himself Greek and Latin. It had to be done in secret; a young man who smuggled a German book to him and was found out was expelled from the community. Very slowly he made contact with others equally intent on opening their minds to the world around them. A rich silk manufacturer gave him a post as accountant in his business so that he was at last sure of a regular income. His treatises on Platonic philosophy gained him general recognition and brought him the friendship of the writer Lessing who invited him to share the editorship of a literary periodical which had great influence on the beginning of the classical age of German literature.

Mendelssohn had arrived in Berlin in the forties of the eighteenth century; thirty years later, his house was the centre of the intellectual life of the town. He was able to provide for his sons the liberal education he had been forced to acquire so painfully by his own efforts. In the traditional manner of the orthodox Jew he kept open house on Friday evening, the beginning of the Sabbath, but contrary to tradition for Jews and Gentiles alike. The refreshments he had to offer were simple, dishes of almonds and raisins and a cup of tea; but the conversation was for the intellectual gourmet. There were a number of such circles now in all of which the women of the house played an equally important rôle, doubling the attraction for the gentile visitor.

Into these circles, Wilhelm and Alexander von Humboldt were introduced by their mathematics teacher, Professor E. G. Fischer, who was also the tutor of the Mendelssohn boys, Joseph and Nathan. Moses Mendelssohn took a special interest in Wilhelm who shared his passion for philosophy while Alexander formed a lasting friendship with the sons. Of equal or even greater importance to him was the introduction to the physician Marcus Herz, a friend of Mendelssohn's who at the age of eighty had become a disciple of the philosopher and scientist Kant. He organized at his house a series of lectures on science and philosophy where Humboldt for the first time in his life had occasion to see the performance of scientific experiments. Herz had a very beautiful and rather flirtatious young wife, Henrietta, of whom the Berliner said: 'If you have not seen the Royal Theatre and Henrietta Herz, you have not seen Berlin.'[1] She liked to gather young and if possible brilliant men around her and soon managed to add the two Humboldts to her collection. They had a lively correspondence, written in the Hebrew alphabet to make the letters incomprehensible to the censor. Alexander used to date his missives from Tegel 'Boredom Castle'. As Henrietta said in her autobiography: 'It was not to be thought of that a young man of his standing should confess in a letter anybody could read that the society of Jewish ladies was more entertaining than a visit to the family seat.'[2]

The intriguing question when and how Alexander became interested in the sciences, has been answered by himself in a letter to the Swiss geographer Pictet: 'Until I was sixteen, I had little inclination for scientific pursuits. I was of a restless disposition and wanted to enter the army. This choice did not please my family who made me take up economics so that I had no opportunity to attend a course of botany and chemistry. I am self-taught in almost all the sciences with which I am now exclusively occupied, and I acquired my knowledge comparatively late in life. I had never so much as heard of botany until 1788 when I made the acquaintance of Willdenow, a young man of my age, who had just published a Flora of Berlin, I never, properly speaking, had any lessons from him but I used to bring him the specimens I collected and he classified them for me. I became passionately interested in botany and in particular in the study of cryptograms. The sight of exotic plants, even of dried specimens in a herbarium, fired my imagination and I longed to see the tropical vegetation in southern countries with my own eyes.'[3]

In the autumn of 1787, the two brothers Humboldt, accompanied by Kunth, started their university life in Frankfurt-on-the-Oder. A small, very provincial garrison town, it had very little to offer to two young men of wide education; scientific training was non-existent. The university library was badly equipped and there was only one small bookshop in the town. Nevertheless, the university, which has long since disappeared, was popular among the sons of the Prussian aristocracy. Alexander, still obedient to his mother's wishes, read economics, a subject which was taken very lightly by the students. It did not require much effort and led to a degree and high office. The teaching was execrable, piecemeal and without cohesion. 'They learn to draw plans for a brandy-distillery, a tar-kiln and a flour mill, they learn the number of threads in the warp and woof of linen and silk, they learn how to make cheese and smelt iron, and how to destroy caterpillars and insect pests; but of the principles of political economy they have not the faintest conception.'[4] As Alexander put it, 'the goddess of Knowledge has no temple here'.

The German student is still free like the wandering scholar of the Middle Ages to move from one university to the other. Thus, the Humboldts left Frankfurt after one winter and sought fresh fields and more eminent teachers in Göttingen. This university, founded in 1737 by George II, had already acquired a great reputation and was one of the most popular in Germany. While Wilhelm went straight to Göttingen from Frankfurt, Alexander interrupted his university life for one year which he spent in Berlin studying factory processes and enlarging his knowledge of Greek. It was at that time that he began to take an interest in botany. In the spring of 1789, he joined his brother in Göttingen after his work in Berlin which corresponded to a present-day course in engineering. The university had then 812 students, of whom 93 belonged to the philosophical faculty which included all the sciences in addition to the humanities and philosophy proper. Among the students were the Duke of Cumberland who afterwards became notorious as King of Hanover; the Duke of Sussex, later president of the Royal Society; the Duc de Broglie and Prince Metternich. A few years later, Thomas Young took a doctor's degree in literature there. He also came under the spell of the Berliner Jewish set; his correspondence with Rachel Varnhagen, one of the intellectual stars of that firmament, is full of the sentimental attitudes characteristic of that period.

Physics was taught by G. C. Lichtenberg, whose name is still remembered as the originator of the terms 'positive' and 'negative' electricity and whose aphorisms may still be read. The leading light among the humanists was C. G. Heyne, one of the founders of classical philology and archaeology. Under his tutelage, Alexander did his first piece of research, a dissertation on the weaving looms of the Greeks and Romans in which he used his technical knowledge to interpret classical technical terms.

The great political event of that year, the beginning of the French Revolution, did not leave the Humboldts unmoved; Wilhelm even made a journey to Paris, 'to be present at the funeral of French despotism'. The ideals expressed by the leading revolutionaries in France made an impression on the brothers which lasted for life and completely determined their political attitudes.

Alexander stayed only one year in Göttingen where he laid the foundations of a systematic knowledge of physics and chemistry. He was beginning to see where his real inclinations lay, and most important of all, he had met George Forster, one of Captain Cook's companions on his second voyage.

George Forster had had an unusual and rather tragic youth. He was descended from a family of Scottish lawyers who had emigrated in the seventeenth century to the wilds of Prussia, settling near Danzig or Gdansk as it is today. Here, they continued to practise law, doing very well for themselves until the stormy life of Reinhold, George's father, destroyed their comfortable and not undistinguished existence. Destined by his father for the law, Reinhold turned to medicine as a short cut to scientific studies but finally compromised on divinity. He took orders but neglected his clerical duties shamefully for his passion for botany, taking his six-year-old boy on long excursions in the country. An official mission to the newly colonized Volga districts in Russia, where he studied the geography and agriculture of the province for a proposed reform of the administration, did not bring him the promised financial rewards and official recognition, partly through political intrigues, partly because he was incapable of being conciliatory when he felt himself in the right. After a short and equally disastrous period as science and language master at the Dissenting Academy in Warrington where he had succeeded Joseph Priestley, he was invited by Lord Sandwich to accompany Captain Cook on his second expedition round the world. His violent temper and intellectual arrogance roused Cook's bitter hostility with the result that Reinhold Forster was again deprived of the fruits of his work.

Since he was a boy of ten, George had shared in his father's Odyssey. Short periods at school in three countries were interspersed by private tuition from his father. From an early age, he had helped by the translation of scientific treatises and travel books to relieve their habitual financial embarrassment. It was George who in his *Voyage round the World* published an account of the expedition's results since his father was prevented from doing it, a book which introduced the German reading public to the newly discovered South Sea world. He was a gentle man with charming manners but erratic and undisciplined after such a childhood. His father's grievances made him equally rebellious against authority. When in 1778 he returned to Germany, his unique experience opened many doors to him. After four years as a professor of natural history in Vilna, where he felt cramped and isolated, he obtained a post as university librarian in Mayence. Discontented and unsettled, he began to take an interest in the political ideas arising just beyond the Rhine. After Mayence had fallen to the French attack in 1792, he became an active member of the provisional government, appointed by the revolutionaries. Two years later, he went to Paris as deputy of the Rhine-German convention and died there in 1794 in his fortieth year. His defection to the enemy camp and his advocacy of the idea that the Rhine is Germany's natural frontier eclipsed his reputation in his country for a long time. He left only a number of short scientific publications behind. The great work on the geography of the newly discovered worlds expected of him never materialized. Everybody who had heard him admitted that he was an atrocious lecturer—and yet he had a name among his contemporaries. In conversation only could he display his unusual range of knowledge; sustained effort and a disciplined ordering of ideas were beyond his capacity.

He had met Humboldt in Göttingen, in the house of Heyne, whose daughter he had married, and found in him an enthusiastic disciple. In the summer of 1790, Forster decided to try once more to obtain redress from the English government for the wrongs, imaginary or not, done to his father and to seek a publisher in London for a projected work on the South Seas.

In the company of Humboldt, he travelled, mainly on foot, down the Rhine to the Netherlands from where they sailed to England. His first sight and taste of the sea made Humboldt an enthusiast for ever; he had the good fortune to be an extremely good sailor. On their way back, they passed through Paris, a Paris intoxicated with the achievements of a year of political liberty, on the eve of the first 'Quatorze Juillet' celebrations. The general enthusiasm and unity of purpose made a lasting impression on the travellers. In his personal affairs, Forster was as unsuccessful as ever but there can be no doubt that his companionship enlarged Humboldt's knowledge immeasurably. For the first time in his life, he saw the past, the present and the future of European civilization. The Gothic vaults and coloured glass of Cologne cathedral after the whitewashed, plain little churches in Brandenburg; the vineyards and fruit trees on the Rhine, the parks and wheat fields in England after the broomlike pine trees; limestone hills and basalts instead of the everlasting sands. In London, he was introduced to Sir Joseph Banks and had occasion to examine his botanical collection; he heard Burke, Pitt and Sheridan in Parliament in one evening. His travels took him north to the Peak district and west to Bristol. One day sufficed for Oxford and none was needed for Cambridge. The budding economist made careful notes on the wool prices in various parts of the country and on the effect on the soil of the rotation of crops.

Over fifty years later, Humboldt gave an assessment of Forster's achievements: 'With him began a new era of scientific travels, that of comparative anthropology and geography. Endowed with a fine aesthetic sensibility, with an ever fresh memory of the impressions which, on Tahiti and other, then more fortunate islands of the South Sea, had fired his imagination (as more recently that of Charles Darwin), George Forster was the first to describe with charm the varying stages of vegetation, the climatic conditions, the nutrients in relation to the customs of people in different localities. Not only in his excellent description of the journey of Captain Cook, even more so in his smaller publications is to be found the germ of something greater, brought to fruition in a more recent period.'[5]

During his stay in Göttingen, Humboldt had become interested in geology and mineralogy, so much so that he decided to obtain a systematic training from a man who was one of the first authorities in this field at the time. Professor A. G. Werner was the founder of Neptunism, the hypothesis that all rocks, even basalt and granite, were the products of sedimentation. He taught mining and mineralogy at the School of Mines in Freiberg in Saxony, the very first institution of that kind which had been founded in 1766 and to which Werner's reputation attracted students from many countries. The training in Freiberg combined theory and practice in an unusual way: Humboldt spent every morning from seven until twelve o'clock in the mines and attended every afternoon five to six lectures. In the evening, he went out to collect mosses and lichens in which he took a particular interest. The lectures covered physics, chemistry, geology and the technique of mining. Even underground, Humboldt botanized, and on discovering that the weak lamp light produced chlorophyll in the vegetation, he made some experiments on the influence of light on plant life. He began to show the spirit of the true experimentalist; any new hypothesis was put to a practical test. It was generally thought at the time that acids destroyed plant life; he immediately set out to show that seeds can be made to germinate in weak solutions of hydrochloric acid. His botanical work led to a publication on the flora of the district, *Flora subterranea Fribergiensis*. He prefaced it by a warning to the reader not to confuse the observed facts with his personal opinions of causes and origins, quoting a saying by Spinoza: 'Thus we see that all theories, destined to explain natural phenomena, are only modes of the imagination, not indicators of natural causes but of the constitution of that imagination.'

Two

Two

EARLY CAREER AND NEW AIMS

HUMBOLDT left Freiberg in February 1792 and by the end of the month he had obtained an appointment in the Mining Department of the Prussian government. Frederick the Great's carefully organized administration had already degenerated into bureaucracy for its own sake. Files with statistical material accumulated and were never looked at. Since his successor, King Frederick William II, was given to dabbling in occult/ism, the surest way to advancement was to profess an admira/tion for any kind of obscurantism. Since real knowledge of the subject and general interests were of no help to a successful career, they were considered undesirable by the men in author/ity. Characteristic of the mood of the time is a story told of one of the ministers. The civil servants in his department had come to congratulate him on his birthday and to hand him a printed address which he refused with the words: 'You know I do not read anything printed; let me have it in writing.' The head of the mining department, minister Heinitz, was an exception; he was an expert in his field and seriously concerned for the development of the mineral resources of Prussia. He had seen service in Brunswick where he reorganized the Harz mines, and in Saxony which owed the mining school in Freiberg to his initiative. Stone quarries, peat and soft coal in Brandenburg, hard coal and iron in Silesia, salt mines—salt was a state monopoly—on the Baltic coast and in the Franconian hills, and the newly acquired mineral deposits in the Margraviate Ansbach/Bayreuth all came under Heinitz's administration. It was originally intended that Humboldt should spend his apprenticeship in the limestone quarries of Rüdersdorf, near

Berlin, which still exist, but he asked to be sent to the badly neglected mines in the Fichtel Mountains, the northernmost and most remote part of the Margraviate.

There, he started his career as a civil servant at the princely salary of eighty pounds a year, a salary which meant semi-starvation for a man without private means. But Humboldt was not without private means and made full use of his independence. After six months of intense activity, he was promoted to the inspectorship of three mining districts in the Fichtel Mountains where he completely reorganized the partly deserted pits, which in the main produced gold and copper. Carried away with enthusiasm, he displayed from the beginning an extraordinary energy and staying power; he rode about the district from one mine to the other, went down the pits and supervised the workings himself, saw to the necessary chemical analyses and the assaying, wrote long reports to Heinitz, made experiments on fire-damp and designed safety lamps which he tried out himself on the spot, not without danger to himself. At one of these trials in a disused working which was filled with gas, he collapsed and had to be dragged out by one of the miners who saw his feet sticking out of the opening. These safety lamps of his invention were in use in the Franconian mines until they were superseded by Sir Humphry Davy's design. Humboldt also experimented with a gas mask which was adopted for practical use.

Another undertaking of his was the organization of a technical school for young miners. He had been struck by the miners' ignorance of their own subject; they could not distinguish between the different ores they handled, and had curious superstitions about the appearance and composition of minerals, but they were eager to learn. Humboldt formed therefore the plan to organize their training and went into immediate action without any official permission, paying for the initial expenses out of his own pocket, since everybody to whom he talked about his idea, advised him against it. The people do not want to learn, they said, and even if they do, they are too hide-bound to understand. Undeterred, Humboldt selected one of the young miners, a local man, to be instructor, whom he trained himself in teaching methods, providing him with books and written instructions. There were good reasons for choosing a local man, apart from the greater expense of obtaining a teacher from elsewhere: he had to be familiar with Franconian mining-rights and usages and with the dialect understood by the boys. The 'free royal mining-school' was opened in the autumn of 1793; to avoid friction with the village school, it was held on Wednesday and Saturday afternoons. Since school attendance during the summer was always slack as the poorer farmers and labourers needed the help of their children on the land, the mining-school functioned only from November until May. Boys who were under the age of twelve years were not accepted but the institution was open to every agricultural labourer and mining apprentice. Attendance was purely voluntary to begin with, and it proved to be greater and more regular than had been expected. The pupils were taught the rudiments of geology and mineralogy, of the course of rivers and the phenomena of the water-table, some mining law, geography of the district and simple mathematical problems of the type that occurs in the construction and maintenance of mines. The ministerial permission for the official establishment of this institution was granted after Humboldt had proved its feasibility and success, and a second school was opened when he had already left the administration. Both these forerunners of further education functioned for a number of years.

In his years in the Fichtel Mountains, Humboldt found time to make an extended investigation into the stimulation of nerves by electrical and chemical means, following up Galvani's work on frog muscles. Galvani believed that the muscular convulsions produced by the applied metal electrodes had their origin in an electric current in the nerves, while Volta thought that the current was due to the contact between two different metals and the frog legs merely served as an electro-scope. The latter theory was beginning to be accepted when Galvani showed that the presence of metals was irrelevant. The muscle contracted when nerve and muscle were brought into contact. At this stage, Humboldt improved on Galvani's technique; he separated the muscle from its nerve and produced contractions of the muscle by simultaneously touching muscle and nerve with a different piece of nerve or by forming a chain of pieces of muscle from one end of the nerve to the other. He based on these observations the hypothesis that the nerves pro-duced a substance which, on entering the muscle, excited it to convulsions. Contact with metals increases the stimulus but is not responsible for it. He was in doubt whether this fluid carried electricity. His investigations were extended to plants, in particular to mimosas, and to animal species leading to the discovery that in hibernation the irritability is increased. He also applied electrodes to open wounds on his back in an attempt to determine the effect of the electric current on the secretion of serum and blood and to find out whether pain could be deadened by an over-stimulation of the nerve.

He continued these physiological studies by investigating the effects of gases and liquids on living animals, using the fre-quency of the heart-beat as an indicator of the reaction. The result was the discovery that breathing will stop if the content of carbon dioxide or hydrocarbonic gases in the air exceeds a certain limit. It did not escape his notice that alcohol and ether act as stimulants in small doses but have a depressing effect when the dose is increased.

Since the description of a series of such electric experiments becomes rather confusing, Humboldt invented a symbolic notation of his own, foreshadowing later developments in physics and chemistry. He assigned the letter 'P' to metals, the letter 'H' to liquids; the symbol 'PP' indicated two identical metal plates in contact and 'Pp' two plates of different metals, again in contact with each other. The term 'nerv. PHPpHP'

stood for the statement that two points of a nerve were connected into a closed circuit in which metals alternated with
each other and with liquids. Arrows and plus and minus signs
expressed the appearance of an effect and the sense of its direction. It is curious that the present-day symbol for the hydrogen
ion concentration 'pH' has a strong resemblance to Humboldt's signs. The publication of his 'Experiments on the
excited muscle and nerve fibre with conjectures on the chemical process of life in the animal and vegetable world' made
some stir at the time. With the discovery, however, of Volta's
pile, the electric battery, Humboldt's just as much as Galvani's
work was considered erroneous; nobody took the trouble to
disentangle his quite original observations on nervous stimulation from those which demonstrated general electrochemical
effects. Humboldt himself felt humiliated that he had not
differentiated sharply enough between strictly physiological and
purely electrical phenomena. He had come very near to the
construction of an electric battery but it had not occurred to
him to try out his combinations of metal plates and liquids in
the absence of physiological tissues. His deep regret is expressed
in a letter to Arago: 'I have observed a great many things as I
am not without ability but I have achieved nothing.'[1]

Twice in these years, Humboldt interrupted his official and
scientific work to undertake political missions, connected with
the war of the Allied German States against the French revolutionary army. Prince Hardenberg, the administrator of the
Margraviate of Ansbach-Bayreuth, who became later a well-
known leader of Prussian politics, impressed by the ability of
his mining inspector, employed him in negotiations with the
French. On his first mission, in 1794, Humboldt took part
under Hardenberg's direction in the preparations for the peace
of Basle which Prussia concluded with France, financially
exhausted since the English subsidies were no longer forthcoming and the Polish rebellion demanded a war on two
fronts. The peace negotiations were begun in secrecy, if the

presence of the king and his ministers in the army headquarters in Frankfurt can be said to have escaped notice. Prussia ceded her possessions on the left bank of the Rhine, and the French withdrew from the right bank. Prussia, Hanover and Hesse-Cassel declared their neutrality, and Austria and the South-German states carried on the war against the French revolutionary troops, incensed by the treacherous defection of their former allies.

Humboldt's rôle in this affair has never been made quite clear; doubtless, it was fairly subordinate. However, he did not miss the opportunity to study the geological formations in the neighbouring districts. His second mission he carried out on his own. It was caused by the invasion in 1796, of Württemberg where Prussia possessed an enclave, the principality of Hohenlohe, the original seat of the Hohenzollern family. Here, a legion of French *émigrés* had been organized in 1791, and the Prussian government feared reprisals from the French troops. It was Humboldt's task to bring about a declaration of neutrality on the basis of the Peace of Basle. He set out, to his own amusement, with one hussar officer, two riflemen and one trumpeter to blow down the walls of Jericho. Still, he was successful; the people of Hohenlohe were allowed to stay in their homes unmolested. This consoling thought was some compensation for being forced to act against his nature and convictions. His success may not have been quite unconnected with the presence of General Desaix who took an interest in chemistry and had heard of Humboldt's safety lamp. He offered him an ascent in the captive balloon used by Desaix for reconnaissance. To his very great regret, Humboldt had to depart and never saw the world from the air.

After his return from this mission, he continued his work on the subterranean atmosphere; he had by this time become convinced that a few, locally scattered observations on the composition of the atmosphere were useless, and he tried to interest other workers in this field in the organization of a network of stations; but the continuing French wars made any such international collaboration impossible.

In 1796, towards the end of his career as a mining inspector, Humboldt became the discoverer of a very striking magnetic anomaly in the Fichtel Mountains. During a cross-country journey, he had noticed a large block of serpentine on the top of a granitic hill. Interested in the alignment of the rock, he approached it with his compass in his hand and saw the needle completely reverse its direction; the serpentine was magnetized in a direction opposed to that of the earth's field. This was the first time that such a reversed polarity had been observed. Humboldt, fascinated by this strange phenomenon, sent some samples to Sir Joseph Banks for analysis who confirmed that the material was weakly magnetic, probably due to the presence of iron oxide in the veins of the mineral. The further history of magnetic observations on the same spot is extremely curious. In 1816, it was found that the reversal of polarity was not so complete over the whole extent of the rock of serpentine as Humboldt had reported. In 1879, the deviation from the magnetic declination normal to that region amounted only to 4° to the west. In 1909, there was no magnetic anomaly at all, but in the vicinity another mass of serpentine was discovered which showed complete reversal of the polarity with an accompanying anomaly in the dip angle. Every observer ascribed these discrepancies to an error in the measurements of his predecessor.

The exciting find in the Fichtel Mountains kept Humboldt's attention on the magnetic properties of rocks, and he met with two more examples in the eruptive strata of the Andes. He had also the good fortune to observe a change of the dip angle after an earthquake in Cumana in Venezuela. At a second visit to the site, ten months later, it had not returned to its original value. He never saw this effect again although this was not his only experience of an earthquake.

During his years in the Franconian mines, his plans for his

own future had taken a definite shape with the gradual discovery of his inclinations and intellectual abilities. From a
vague longing to see new countries they had become the fixed
determination to take part in a scientific expedition. His first
definite allusion to his intentions was occasioned by his proposed promotion to Berlin with a salary of £300 in 1794. He
refused to accept the new post explaining that he intended to
resign in two years and to go on an expedition to 'Russia,
Siberia or elsewhere'. A year later, he was most pressingly asked
to go to Silesia as Director of Mining; Humboldt refused. The
offer was repeated and Humboldt refused again. In his letter
to Heinitz he now became more explicit: he had always looked
upon his mining activities as merely a preparation for his real
purpose, that of a geological and geophysical expedition. He
had postponed his resignation on account of the illness of his
mother who suffered from cancer, but was determined to
leave public service in the spring of 1797, whatever the circumstances. Heinitz, who wanted to retain him in office at
any cost, now proposed to grant him a paid leave of absence
for a period of four to five years. Humboldt, however, felt that
the straitened finances of the country forbade him to accept this
offer. The death of his mother in 1796 set him free; he had
been distressed at her terrible illness but he had to admit that
he suffered no personal loss. 'We were for ever strangers.'

His plans were by now well defined. 'I shall collect instruments and prepare myself for several years. I want to stay in
Italy for twelve to eighteen months to make a thorough study
of volcanoes, then go via Paris to England where I might easily
remain another year for I do not want to rush my preparations,
and then on an English ship to India.'[2] He did, in fact, spend
two years on his preliminary studies but not in Italy and not in
England, and he never went to India, although twice in his
life he came very near to a realization of this intention. Politics,
the curse of modern man, prevented the plan every time.

In February 1797, he finally sent in his resignation, joined his brother in Jena and went with the whole family to Dresden. There, Wilhelm Humboldt continued his philological and philosophical studies while Alexander practised geodetic and astronomical observations with a Hadley sextant and examined the collections of Spanish and American minerals in the Royal Library. The social standing of the Humboldts gave them entrée into official circles; the connexions Alexander acquired during his stay in Dresden became of the greatest importance to him at a moment when his plans for an expedition seemed near to complete failure.

But in Saxony life looked very promising; he was now a well-to-do man by the standards of his time and country. His share of their inheritance came to £17,000, providing him with a yearly income of nearly £700. With the intention of spending the winter in Italy, the whole family, including Wilhelm's small children, set out for Vienna where they continued a similar existence. Wilhelm pored over the medieval manuscripts in the Imperial Library; Alexander studied the magnificent collections of herbaria and the exotic plants in the gardens of Schönbrunn. The personal contact with other scientists also played an important role in his self-imposed apprenticeship. There was Porth, a professor of medicine who owned a very fine collection of tropical plants and of anatomical specimens in whose preparation he was a master. Very rich, he was also very eccentric; completely engrossed in his scientific activities, he had reduced daily life to its last essentials. He himself and his possessions were all housed in one room, one corner of which was used as a chemical laboratory. Next to his bench he bred chickens for physiological experiments in the shadow of an antique statue of one of Niobe's sons. He dressed in a kind of union suit of his own invention, a sleeved waistcoast ending in breeches and stockings. Just then he was occupied with the design of a hat which turned into an umbrella when he pulled a string. He did not like to burden his organism with food during the day; one meal, taken at ten o'clock in the evening, provided the necessary fuel for his enthusiastic activities.

During that summer it became more and more obvious that the Napoleonic campaigns would make the Italian journey an impossibility. Paris was therefore chosen as the next aim for the whole family. In the end, when Wilhelm set out, Alexander did not accompany him since an old friend of his, Leopold von Buch whom he had met at Freiberg, came to Vienna to join him. Buch, who became afterwards a very well-known geologist, was also rich and cranky; he was extremely shy and unsociable to the point of being impossible. 'I was so pleased to see him,' wrote Humboldt, 'he is brilliant and an excellent ob-server but his manners—as if he came from the moon. His journey here, all by himself, has made him worse again. I have taken him with me to see people but it did not turn out well. Usually he puts on his glasses and goes and studies the cracks in the stove-tiles on which he is dead keen, or he slinks round the walls like a hedgehog and looks at the skirting-board. On his own he is an interesting and charming person—a treasure of knowledge from which I profit.'[3] To gain as much as possible from the knowledge and experience of his friend, Humboldt accompanied Buch to Salzburg and the surrounding district, the region of salt mines. There they spent the winter in an orgy of magnetic, geographical and meteorological measurements. Humboldt practised assiduously with a twelve-inch sextant by Wright; he admired its performance but complained bitterly of its heaviness. Their geodetic observations led to a great im-provement over the existing maps of the country. Equally thorough were the meteorological investigations: every day at the same hours determinations were carried out of the baro-metric pressure, the temperature, the humidity, the oxygen and carbon-dioxide contents and the electric charge of the air. On the basis of the experience gained in these months, Humboldt formulated his programme for meteorological observations which became eventually an universally accepted procedure.

In November, the notorious Lord Bristol invited Humboldt to join, as a scientist, an expedition he planned to make to Egypt. He had already secured the participation of the archaeologist Hirt from Berlin and of the French scholar Savary who, from an extended stay, knew Egypt very well. Artists were to make drawings and paintings of the scenery and the historical monuments; and, last but not least, Madame Dennis and Countess Lichtenau, musicians and a superlative cook were to provide the pleasures of a civilized life. They intended to sail in two ships across the Mediterranean and up the Nile. Countess Lichtenau, the former mistress of Frederick William II, found herself almost immediately unable to join since, on the death of the king, that same November, her position at home became all too precarious. Humboldt accepted the invitation with some misgivings. 'I may be blamed for associating with the noble lord; he is the eccentric of eccentrics. I have only once seen him, on one of those journeys he made on horseback from Pyrmont to Naples. I realise that it might be difficult to live in peace with him. But travelling at my own expense I retain my independence and do not risk anything. If it goes too much against my grain, I can leave. Besides he is a man of genius, and I cannot let such a wonderful opportunity pass. I may be able to do something for meteorology.'[4] Humboldt, intent on the realization of his great plans, embarked immediately on a study of Egyptian archaeology; and even though this projected journey came to nothing, he found his knowledge very useful when in the end he came to see the pyramids of the New World instead. He started for Paris in the spring of 1798 in order to say farewell to his brother and to provide himself with the necessary scientific instruments, already disturbed by rumours of a forthcoming invasion of Egypt by Napoleon.

Before he even arrived in France, the rumours had become reality. The French fleet had sailed accompanied by a small army of scientists and scholars who had been invited to the expedition in greatest secrecy. Lord Bristol was arrested in Milan, suspected of being a secret agent of the British government, and had to spend the next eighteen months in jail. And Humboldt arrived in Paris with his plans for the future in ruins. But, flexible as always, he immediately threw himself into new activities. At that time, the great triangulation of France was in full swing; the last measurements of the meridian between Melun and Lieursaint were just being made which served as a basis for the length of the Paris metre. Whenever he was downcast by disappointments Humboldt turned to more and more science. He was introduced to Delambre who was in charge of the geodetic team and enthusiastically plied the sextant with them, spending some weeks of glorious summer weather in the countryside. At that time, when Napoleon was on the crest of the wave, the weather favoured even his scientific enterprises.

The French scientific world, after having given its hostages to politics during the Terror—Lavoisier and Condorcet had been its victims—was now very much in official favour. Napoleon himself who, as a gunner, took an interest in mathematics, was in the habit of attending the meetings of the Institut de France. Men whose names are still very much alive, Laplace, Lagrange, Borda, Cuvier, St. Hilaire, Haüy discussed the latest methods and ideas with Humboldt and advised him on equipment and points of investigation.

He also was for the second time invited to become the member of a scientific expedition whose eventual abandonment caused him a much greater pain than his first disappointment. This time, the French government planned an expedition to the Pacific regions which was to last five years and to include extensive investigations on land and sea. At first it was intended to put the leadership into the hands of the aged Bougainville, but finally Captain Baudin was put in charge. In the first two years, the South American countries, Mexico and California, were to be studied; the third year was to be spent in the Pacific Ocean with the object of reaching the South Pole, the fourth year in Madagascar, and the fifth in New Guinea. Humboldt, on the advice of Borda, wanted to devote most of his time to magnetic measurements and was invited to choose all the instruments he might need from the national collections. He was in a ferment of excitement. But the dream had only lasted a fortnight when Napoleon decided to postpone the expedition indefinitely as the Egyptian cam, paign demanded all his financial resources. Humboldt, dis, tressed but determined on his own plans, immediately made up his mind to take ship from Marseilles to Algiers, to spend the winter in the Constantine district of the Atlas and join in the spring the caravan from Tripolis to Mecca. He intended to leave it in Cairo for a journey through Egypt in the wake of the French army. He found a companion in the botanist Aimé Bonpland, who had been one of the scientists chosen by Baudin. They finished their preparations and set out for Mar, seilles in October 1798 where they had to wait for the arrival of the packet,boat; two long months passed before the news came of her shipwreck on the coast of Portugal. An attempt to sail on a hired ship to Tunis failed; the authorities, perturbed by rumours of an impending revolt in North Africa, refused to grant them the necessary visa.

Thwarted again, the two travellers now decided to go to Spain where they hoped to find in the spring a ship bound for Smyrna. At the end of December, they started out on foot along the Mediterranean coast, crossed the Pyrenees at their eastern end and made their way through Catalonia to Madrid. On the six weeks of their journey, Humboldt found it difficult to carry out his habitual daily observations. In the small Spanish towns, the people collected round him and booed whenever he set up his instruments. In the end he was forced to take his readings at night. These observations which were extended right across the country to the Galician coast made an important contribution to the geographical knowledge of the time. The existing maps were found to be quite inaccurate, and Humboldt was the first to discover that the interior of Spain forms a high plateau. Just before his departure from Paris, he had been instructed by Laplace in his method to determine altitudes by measurements of barometric pressure: the Spanish results proved its usefulness, which, in essentials, has lasted to the present day.

Arrived in Madrid, Humboldt called immediately on the representatives of the various European courts, trying to rouse their interests in their plans. He had no success with his own country; the Prussian envoy did not lift a finger for him, but Forell, the Saxon chargé d'affaires, who had an inclination for science, interceded for him with the Spanish minister Luis d'Urquijo who was known to be liberally minded. At last, the world opened to Humboldt; he was given permission to travel in the then Spanish colonies in South America. An audience with the king followed, in which Humboldt explained his purposes of an extensive survey of the royal possessions and the advantages to the Spanish government of such an investigation. The royal letters of recommendation ensured him access everywhere. These permits were quite exceptional; the Spanish government kept its colonies completely shut off from contact with the outside world. They were not even allowed to trade with any other than the mother country, a regulation which had led to a flourishing smuggling trade with the nonSpanish West Indies. Since the expedition of de la Condamine in 1735, no foreign scientist had visited South American soil. Humboldt's triumph was sensational.

In May 1799 the two travellers left Madrid for Corunna, still on foot and still continuing their observations until their arrival in the harbour where they boarded the packetboat *Pizarro* bound for Cuba. Her captain had orders to put in at Teneriffe to give Humboldt and Bonpland the opportunity of visiting the island and climbing the Pic. Warned that an English patrol had been sighted off the Spanish coast, they set sail in haste, and on the 5th of June 1799 they were under way.

Humboldt was then in his thirtieth year. After a late start he had proved in a meteoric career his independent and original mind and an unlimited capacity for work which allowed him to combine scientific research in various fields with his adminis- trative activities. Even his friends found it alarming that he never wrote less than three books at a time. His physiological and botanical investigations, his work on the composition of the atmosphere had gained him some reputation. He had become increasingly self-confident; in fact, he was sometimes called cocksure. Vanity and the desire to shine were his main faults, as his brother had warned him; in his publications he did not always show the necessary respect of the novice for established authority. His embarkation on a two-man expedi- tion might have appeared as the irresponsibility of conceit rather than the resolution of a man of genius.

Three

~~~~~~~~~~~~~~~~~~~~~~~~~~~

THE LLANOES

HUMBOLDT and Bonpland spent five years in the New World travelling in the Spanish possessions on foot, on mules, on boats, surveying and collecting. In a journey of 6,000 miles, they had the unique opportunity to study low-lying plains and extensive mountain ranges, oceanic currents and one of the most enormous river systems of the world, active and extinct volcanoes. In truth, it was a new world: a tropical climate with well-marked seasons, earthquakes and meteoric showers which set the night alight; flora and fauna, the very stars in the sky were new.

Spain's American colonies reached at that time from the 38th degree northern latitude to the 42nd degree southern latitude. All of Central America, the majority of the West Indian islands, and the whole of South America with the exception of Brazil, Patagonia, and Tierra del Fuego, were possessions of the Spanish crown as well as nearly a third of the present-day territory of the United States. The whole vast empire, divided up into kingdoms under various viceroys, was rigidly controlled by the Spanish government. The Creole landowners, the descendants of the original conquerors, were not allowed any part in the administration or the defence; every army officer, every civil servant was sent over from Spain and returned there at the end of his term of office. The whole army comprised only 2,000 men, and Humboldt was staggered to see some of the Indian troops in the Llanoes of Venezuela armed with bows and arrows. No attempts had been made at a systematic development of the vast tracts of unbelievably fertile soil, for there was no immigration of European peasants; the cheap labour demanded by the landowners was provided by imported Negro slaves since the indigenous Indians had not shown themselves amenable to a forced settlement on the land. Spain had a complete monopoly of the total produce of the colonies: all imports came from Spain, all exports went there in large bi-annual convoys. Confiscation of all his possessions and even capital punishment threatened any person bold enough to trade with another country. All Spain had ever wanted from her overseas territory was gold, or at least silver, although the exploitation of the mines was hampered by the reluctance of the far-distant government to tolerate the development of a middle class. But it was becoming impossible to confine a country behind its frontiers. The ports on the northern coast of South America did a nice little trade in contraband with the British and French West Indies. And in the process of exporting produce, they brought back news and ideas from the outside world. The Creoles, who prided themselves on their pure blood just as much as the aristocracy of the old country, were beginning to be resentful of their passive role, and the newly-won independence of their North American neighbours drove them into rebellious action. The first abortive rising took place in Caracas two years before Humboldt's arrival.

Scientific exploration of the country had been equally discouraged by the Spanish government; within three centuries there had only been six expeditions by Spaniards and foreigners who had been mainly concerned with coastal surveys. The last of those was that of the unfortunate Malaspina who became a victim of the Spanish obscurantism. The Marqués de Malaspina, an admiral of the Spanish fleet, had been put in charge of a flotilla in 1789 for the purpose of mapping the northern coast of western America and of searching for a north-west passage. He was successful in his survey but failed, as many others after him, to find the north-west passage. On his return to Spain in 1795, he was arrested as politically suspect and imprisoned in the fortress of San Antonio near Corunna.

There was no trial and he was never heard of again. He was simply treated as a man suffering from an incurable and conta/ gious mental disease. When Humboldt sailed out of the harbour of Corunna, his eyes kept coming back to San Antonio: 'At the moment of my departure from Europe and on my way to coun/ tries which this famous traveller had so successfully explored, I could have wished to turn my thoughts to happier subjects.'[1]

The first eighteen months of his expedition, Humboldt spent in Venezuela. After three months in Cuba at the beginning of 1801, he returned to Cartagena on the South American main/ land to explore Colombia, Ecuador, and Peru, a journey which lasted until February 1803. He then sailed to Mexico to whose survey he devoted another year. A second stay in Cuba in the spring of 1804 was followed by a visit to the United States. In July of 1804 he sailed from Philadelphia, arriving in Bordeaux on the 3rd of August 1804. Venezuela meant a study of the enormous plains, the Llanoes, and of the curiously intertwined river system of the Orinoco and the Rio Negro. The explora/ tion of the mountain ranges and volcanoes of the Andes was carried out from 1801 until 1803 where Humboldt's route was very much that of the present/day Panamerican Highway. Humboldt recorded the first part of his journey in his *Personal narrative of travels to the equinoctial regions of the new continent during the years 1799 to 1804.* The five volumes of this work comprise only the exploration of Venezuela, and, in spite of the title, everything personal, the physical efforts, the occasional dangers are only touched upon; in the main, it is a clinically detached account of scenery and climate, of the people, settlers and natives, and the administration of the country. A highly edu/ cated and literate scientist, who is by no means unimpression/ able, tries to describe the grandeurs of the scenery but never forgets to relate the character of the landscape to the geophysical and meteorological causes. And there is no factor, from the history of the country to the constellations in the sky, to which he did not give attention. Even the results of his measurements are not omitted, although they are banished to appendices. It was his intention to combine the subjective with the factual. He abhorred the facile emotionalism of his time as 'mushiness of the soul'. The novelty of the subject and the combination of scientific accuracy and literary representation made a great impression on the public; how deep it was, can be seen from Darwin's letter to J. Hooker: 'I shall never forget that my whole course of life is due to having read and re-read as a youth his *Personal Narrative*.'[2]

After a week's stay on Teneriffe, where Humboldt climbed the Pic, the boat arrived in Cumana in Venezuela on the 16th of July. The first sight of tropical nature completely over-whelmed Humboldt; a letter sent off the very next day to his brother, expresses his enthusiasm. 'We remain a few months in the province of Caracas; we are here in a divine country. Wonderful plants; electric eels, tigers, armadilloes, monkeys, parrots; and many, many, real, half-savage Indians, a hand-some and interesting race. The proximity of snow-covered mountains makes Caracas the coolest and healthiest place to stay in; a climate like Mexico, and although visited by Jacquin, one of the most unknown parts of the world if one goes into the interior of the mountains. . . . The town is still half buried in debris; the famous earthquake of Quito in 1797 equally destroyed Cumana. The town lies on a gulf as beautiful as that of Toulon, behind an amphitheatre of thickly wooded moun-tains, five to eight thousand feet high. . . . What trees! Coco-nut trees, 50 to 60 feet high; *poinciana pulcherrima* with a foot high bouquet of magnificent, bright-red flowers; pisang and a host of trees with enormous leaves and scented flowers, as big as the palm of a hand, of which we knew nothing. . . . And what colours in birds, fish, even crayfish (sky blue and yellow)! We rush around like the demented; in the first three days we were quite unable to classify anything; we pick up one object to throw it away for the next. Bonpland keeps telling me that he will go mad if the wonders doe not cease soon.'[3]

The months until February 1800, the explorers spent in the comparatively populous and cultivated country between Cumana and Puerto Cabello where Bonpland found a rich field for his botanical activities. Humboldt, as habitual with him, packed an enormously varied amount of observations into his days and nights. His main interests were directed towards a geographical survey of the country and continuous meteoro-logical measurements. The very regular rise and fall of the thermometer and barometer in those regions made the tropical climate the ideal field for a meteorological investigation. 'How can I describe to you the purity, the beauty and the splendour of the sky here; I often read the vernier of my little sextant by the light of Venus. Venus plays here the role of the moon. It shows big, luminous haloes, two degrees in diameter, of the most beautiful rainbow colours even when the air is completely pure and the sky quite blue. I believe that here the stars offer the most magnificent spectacle. Towards the equator, the beautiful constellations of the north are lost to sight. But the southern firmament has its own beauties. Sagittarius, the Southern Crown, the Southern Cross possess beautiful stars and Centaur can be compared to our Orion, its constellation is so beautiful; I make my observations here at an altitude which makes me groan and sweat.

'Another singular and marvellous phenomenon is the atmo-spheric tide which I observed at once, the second day of my arrival. You know the paper by Francis Balfour and John Farquhar in the fourth volume of the *Asiatic Researches*. These atmospheric tides are here more regular than in Bengal and obey quite different laws. The thermometer is constantly in motion. The mercury falls from 9 o'clock in the morning until four o'clock in the afternoon. Then it rises until 11 o'clock, falls again until 4.30, rises until 9 o'clock. The weather is quite immaterial, rain, wind, hurricane, storms, the moon, etc., nothing changes this process. There are four tides in 24 hours; the shortest are those of the night. The barometer reaches its highest stand three hours before and eleven hours after its passage through the meridian. It seems therefore that the sun alone has an influence on the rise and fall. The regularity is so precise that at 9.15 the thermometer has already fallen. I have collected hundreds of these observations and one day I shall have thousands. I have not observed any effect of earthquakes on the barometer. But the moon does visibly disperse the clouds here. . . . Be indulgent with my astronomical work. Remember, it is only a by-product of my journey; I am only an apprentice in astronomy and did not learn to handle the instruments until two years ago. I have undertaken the journey at my expense. Such an expedition, made by a private person who is by no means wealthy, done for his own pleasure and instruction cannot be compared with those undertaken by governments, royally endowed and for which an entire society of scholars is assembled to make investigations in all the branches of knowledge.'[4]

A visit to the Indian missions in the hinterland gave him the opportunity to experiment with electric eels, a living electrical machine. He experienced his first earthquake, and an extraordinary display of meteorites in November directed his attention to the periodicity of meteoric showers. His observations on the connection between aridity of the soil and the destruction of forests are still rediscovered and again forgotten. 'Felling the trees which cover the sides and tops of mountains, provokes in every climate two disasters for future generations: a want of fuel and a scarcity of water. Trees are surrounded by a permanently cool and moist atmosphere due to the evaporation of water vapour from the leaves and their radiation in a cloudless sky. They have an effect on the incidence of springs not as was long believed by a peculiar attraction for the atmospheric vapour but because they shelter the soil from the direct action of the sun and thereby lessen the evaporation of the rainwater. When forests are destroyed, as they are everywhere in America by the hands of the European planters, the springs are reduced in volume or dry up entirely. The river beds, now dry during part of the year, are transformed into torrents whenever there is a heavy rainfall in the mountains. Turf and moss disappear with the brushwood from the sides of the hills; the rainwater rushing down no longer meets with any obstructions. Instead of slowly raising the level of the rivers by progressive filtration, it cuts furrows into the ground, carries down the loosened soil and produces those sudden inundations which devastate the country. It follows that the destructions of forests, the lack of springs and the existence of torrents are three closely connected phenomena.'[5]

The character of the Llanoes and the hunt for electric eels have been described by Humboldt in his *Aspects of Nature*:

A widely extended and apparently interminable plain stretches from the southern base of the lofty granitic crest which in the youth of our planet, when the Caribbean gulf was formed, braved the intrusion of the waters. On leaving the mountain valleys of Caracas and the island studded lake of Tacarigua whose surface reflects the trunks of banana palms, behind him fields of the bright and tender green of the Tahitian sugar cane or the darker growth of the cocoa groves, the traveller sees before him steppes receding until they vanish in the far horizon. Neither hill nor cliff rises, like an island in the ocean, to break the uniformity of the boundless plain; only here and there broken strata of limestone, several hundred square miles in extent, appear noticeably higher than the surroundings. 'Banks' is the name given to them by the natives, as if language instinctively recalled the more ancient epoch when these plateaux were shoals and the steppes themselves were the bottom of a great Mediterranean sea. Here, no oasis recalls the memory of earlier inhabitants; no carved stone, no ruined building, no fruit tree, once cultivated but now wild, speaks of the art or industry of former generations. Estranged from the destinies of mankind and riveting attention only to the present moment, this corner of the earth appears as a wild theatre for the free development of animal and vegetable life. The steppe extends from the Caracas coast chain to the forests of Guyana, and from the snow mountains of Merida to the great delta formed by the Orinoco at its mouth. To the south-west a branch is prolonged like an inlet of the sea to the lonely mountain to which the excited imagination of the Spanish soldiers gave the name of Paramo de la Suma Paz—the seat of perfect peace.

Like the greater part of the desert of the Sahara, the Llanoes are in the torrid zone: during one half of the year they are desolate like the Libyan sand waste; during the other they appear as a grassy plain, resembling many of the steppes of Central Asia.

It is a highly interesting though difficult task of general geography to compare the natural conditions of widely separated regions, and to draw the results with a few strokes. The causes which diminish both heat and dryness in the New World (as compared with the old) are manifold and in some respects as yet only partially understood. Among these may be classed the narrowness and deep indentation of the American land in the northern part of the tropical zone where in consequence the atmosphere resting on a liquid base, does not produce so heated an ascending current; —the extension of the continent towards the poles;—the expanse of ocean over which the trade winds sweep freely acquiring thereby a cooler temperature;—the flatness of the eastern coasts;—currents of cold sea water from the antarctic regions which, moving from the south-west to the north-east, first strike the coast of Chile in the parallel of 35° southern latitude and advance along the coast of Peru as far north as the cape of Pariña and then turn suddenly to the west;—the numerous high mountain chains, rich in springs, and whose snow-covered peaks, rising high above the strata of clouds, cause descending currents of cold air to roll down their slopes;—the abundance of rivers of enormous width which after many loops reach the far distant coast;—grasslands which do not become as heated as sands;—impenetrable forests occupying the alluvial plains situated immediately below the equator, protecting with their shade the soil beneath from the direct influence of the rays of the sun, and emitting in the interior of the country at a great distance from the mountains and the ocean vast quantities of moisture, partly absorbed and partly due to the evaporation of the plants;—all these circumstances confer upon the flat parts of America a climate which contrasts wonderfully with that of Africa. . . .

The Llanoes are indeed well suited to the rearing of cattle, but the care of animals yielding milk was almost unknown to the original inhabitants of the new continent. . . . The American race (which with the exception of the Eskimoes is one and the same from 65° North to 55° South) has not passed from the state of hunters to that of agriculture through the intermediate stage of a pastoral life. . . . Since the discovery of the new continent, the Llanoes have become habitable to man. In order to facilitate communication between the Orinoco country and the coasts, towns have been built here and there on the banks of the streams which flow through the steppe. The rearing of cattle has begun over all parts of these vast regions. Huts, built of reeds tied together with thongs and covered with skin, are placed at distances of a day's journey from each other; numberless herds of oxen, horses and mules, estimated at the peaceful time of my journey at a million and a half, roam the steppe. The immense increase in the number of these animals, originally brought by man from the old continent, is the more remarkable from the number of dangers with which they have to contend.

When under the vertical rays of the unclouded sun, the charred covering turf crumbles to dust, the hardened soil cracks as from the shock of an earthquake. If at such times two opposing currents of air whose conflict produces a rotary motion, come in contact with the soil, the plain assumes a strange and singular aspect. Like cone-shaped clouds whose apexes descend to the earth, the sand rises through the rarified air in the electrically charged centre of the whirling current, resembling the loud waterspout dreaded by the experienced mariner. The lowering sky diffuses a dim, almost straw-coloured light on the desolate plain. The horizon draws suddenly nearer; the steppe seems to contract and with it the heart of the wanderer. The hot, dusty particles which fill the air, increase its suffocating heat, and the east wind blowing over the long-heated soil brings with it no refreshment but rather a still more burning glow. The pools which the yellow fading branches of the palm-trees had protected from evaporation, now gradually disappear. As in the icy north the animals become torpid with cold, so here, under the influence of the parching drought, the crocodile and the boa become motionless and fall asleep, deeply buried in the dry mud. Everywhere, the death-threatening drought prevails, and yet by the play of the refracted rays of light pro-ducing the phenomenon of the mirage, the thirsty traveller is pursued by the illusive image of a cool rippling watery mirror. The distant palm bush, apparently raised by the influence of the contact of unequally heated and therefore unequally dense strata of air, hovers above the ground from which it is separated by a narrow intervening margin. Half con-cealed by the dark clouds of dust, restless with the pain of thirst and hunger, the horses and cattle roam around; the cattle lowing dismally, and the horses stretching out their long necks and snuffing the wind if by chance a moister current may betray the neighbourhood of a not wholly dried-up pool. Shrewder and more cunning, the mule has found a different mode of alleviating his thirst. The ribbed and spherical melon cactus conceals under its prickly envelope a watery pith. The mule first strikes the prickles aside with his forefeet and then warily puts his lips to the plant and drinks the cool juice. But resort to this vegetable fountain is not always without danger, and one sees many animals that have been lamed by the prickles of the cactus.

When the burning heat of the day is followed by the coolness of the night, even then the horses and cattle cannot rest. Enormous bats suck their blood like vampires during their sleep or attach themselves to their backs, causing festering wounds in which mosquitoes and a host of stinging insects settle. . . . At length, after the long drought, the welcome season of the rains arrives; and then how suddenly is the scene changed! The deep blue of the hitherto cloudless sky becomes lighter; at night, the dark space in the constellation of the Southern Cross is hardly distinguish-able; the soft, phosphorescent light of the Magellanic clouds fades away; even the stars in Aquila and Ophiuchus in the zenith shine with a trembling and less planetary light. A single cloud appears in the south, like a distant mountain, rising perpendicularly from the horizon. Gradu-ally, the increasing vapours spread like mist over the sky, and now a distant thunder ushers in the life-restoring rain. Hardly has the surface of the earth received the refreshing moisture than the previously barren steppe begins to emit a sweet smell and to clothe itself with grasses. The herbaceous mimosas, with renewed sensitivity to the influence of light, unfold their drooping, slumbering leaves to greet the rising sun. . . . The horses and cattle now graze in full enjoyment of life. The tall springing grass hides the beautifully spotted jaguar who, lurking in safe concealment, and measuring carefully the distance of a single bound, springs cat-like as the Asiatic tiger on his passing prey.

Sometimes (so the aborigines relate) on the edge of the swamps, the moistened clay is seen to blister and rise slowly in a kind of mound; then with a violent noise like the outbreak of a small mud-volcano, the heaped-up earth is thrown high into the air. The onlooker acquainted with the meaning of this spectacle flies, for he knows a gigantic water snake or a scaly crocodile will come out, awakened from a torpid state by the first fall of rain.

The rivers which bound the plain to the south, the Arauca, Apure and Payara become gradually swollen; and now nature forces the same animals, who in the first half of the year panted with thirst on the dry and dusty soil, to lead an amphibious life. A portion of the steppe shows the aspect of a vast inland sea. The brood mare retires with its foals to the higher banks which stand like islands above the surface of the lake. Every day, the space remaining dry becomes smaller. The animals, crowded together, swim about for hours in search of other pasture and feed sparingly on the tops of the flowering grasses rising above the seething surface of the dark-coloured water. Many foals are drowned, and many are surprised by the crocodiles, killed by a stroke of their powerful notched tails and devoured. . . .

But the crocodile and the jaguar are not the only attackers of the South American horses; they have also a dangerous enemy among fishes. The marshy waters of Bera and Rastro are filled with numerous electric eels which can at will send a powerful discharge from any part of their slimy, yellow-spotted bodies. These gymnoti are five to six feet in length and are strong enough to kill the largest animals when they discharge their nervous organs in the right direction.

The former route from Uritucu through the steppe had to be changed because the gymnoti had increased to such numbers in a small stream that many horses were drowned in the ford, either from the effect of the shocks or from fright. All other fish fly the vicinity of these formidable eels. Even the fisherman, fishing from the high bank, is afraid that the damp line will conduct the shock from a distance. Thus, in these regions, electric fire erupts from the depth of the waters.

The capture of the gymnoti is a picturesque sight. Mules and horses are driven into a marsh which is closely surrounded by Indians, until the unwonted noise and the disturbance drive the pugnacious fish to attack. They can be seen to swim about like serpents and trying cunningly to glide under the bellies of the horses. Many are stunned by the force of the invisible blows; others with manes standing on end, foaming and with wild terror in their eyes, try to fly from the raging storm. But the Indians, armed with long poles of bamboo, drive them back into the middle of the pool. Gradually the fury of the unequal struggle begins to slacken. Like clouds which have discharged their electricity, the wearied fish scatter; long repose and abundant food are needed to replace the galvanic force which they have expended. Their shocks become weaker and weaker. Terrified by the noise of the trampling horses, they timidly approach the bank where they are wounded by harpoons and cautiously drawn on shore by non-conducting pieces of dry wood.

Humboldt performed some simple experiments with living eels on the spot and killed and dissected them, investigations in line with his work on the stimulation of nerves. Various curious facts were soon established: the electrical discharge from the fish does not affect the electrometer and no sparks were observed on their bodies when they were irritated in the dark. Magnetic effects were equally absent. Although the skin of the gymnotus is covered with mucus, a good conductor of electricity, it does not electrocute itself, a fact which greatly puzzled Humboldt, and which still puzzles us today. The shocks may come from one part of the body or from the whole surface; it can be felt by a person standing on an insulator and touching it with one finger only—the connexion to earth lies presumably over the moist skin of the eel. Later observers, who managed to keep live eels in a tank, found that they were able to kill fish at a distance through the water. Galvani had already shown that all electrical action is stopped if the brain is injured or the nerves leading to the electric organs are severed: the discharge is an act of will and not a mere reflex action. Humboldt made a cut through the middle of the fish and observed that only the front part remained capable of producing an electric effect. He closes his discussion with a conclusion not far removed from modern ideas: 'It will perhaps be found that in most animals every contraction of the muscle fibre is preceded by a discharge from the nerve into the muscle, and that the simple contact of heterogeneous substances is a source of movement and of life in all organised beings.'[6]

I. Rio Meta: sketches from Humboldt's diary, part IV (diary of the navigation on the rivers Apure, Orinoco, Casiquiare and Rio Negro), German State Library, Berlin

Four

THE ORINOCO

TRAVELLING in a south-westerly direction through the immense plains of the Llanoes, Humboldt and Bonpland with their instruments and collections arrived on the 26th of March 1800 on the banks of the Apure, a tributary of the Orinoco. For the next three months, they exchanged the horizons of the grasslands for the dense forests of this vast river system. Accompanied by Don Nicolas Sotto, the brother-in-law of the governor of the province of Varinas, they started their journey from San Fernando in a large sailing canoe with four Indian rowers and one pilot. A cabin had been erected near the stern under a roof of leaves; ox hides stretched tight over wooden frames served as tables and benches. At night, a camp on the river bank provided shelter for their hammocks—a word we owe to the Indians of those regions—and a large fire kept the jaguars away. They made their way down the Apure and up the Orinoco past the cataracts of the Atures and Maipures where Father Zea of the mission of the Atures joined them, to the confluence with the little river Atabapo. A short portage brought them from the upper end of the Atabapo to one of the source rivers of the Rio Negro, the Guainia which they followed downstream to San Carlos. They now retraced their way to the mouth of the Casiquiare. From there they travelled up this river beyond its junction with the Orinoco to the settlement of Esmeralda. The belligerency of the Guaharibo Indians prevented them from reaching the source of the Orinoco. They completed their survey of the river system by sailing down the Orinoco all the way to Ciudad Bolívar (in Humboldt's time called San Thomas d'Angostura) whence they returned to

Barcelona through the Llanoes, arriving on the 26th of August.

A sudden squall on the Orinoco nearly put an end to the explorers and their exploration soon after their departure from San Fernando. The river has a width there of over two miles in the dry season. The boat filled with water, and the Indians started to jump out, trying to swim to the bank. Bonpland, who could not swim, implored Humboldt to save himself. It was an ugly situation; the nearest land was half a mile away and the water was alive with crocodiles. There would have been no escape either through the jungle of trees and lianas surrounding them. In this dangerous moment, a gust of wind filled their sail and righted the boat, and only a few books and some food were lost.

The next morning they were overtaken by a family of Caribs who had come all the way from the mouth of the Orinoco, four hundred miles away, to collect turtle eggs, an annual pleasurable event. These tortoises come in huge flocks—Humboldt estimated their number at about a million—to lay their eggs in the earth below the sand of the shore at the time of the lowest water level, just before the vernal equinox. This is the occasion for a more than local fair; Indian tribes, several hundreds of them, distinguishable by their war-paint, travel hundreds of miles to an encampment on the *boca de tortuga*, an island in the river. Some white traders turn up as well, and the missionaries from south of the cataracts, to see white faces and hear the news from the outside world; the rest of the year they pass their lives grumbling about the heat and the mosquitoes.

The Indians staked out their claims on the hunting ground like mining prospectors and worked over the lots in fierce competition with the sun which hatched young tortoises as fast as the men could dig up the sand. The eggs were rendered down on the spot for the oil contained in them. It was used as cooking fat and to light the oil lamps, but the crude procedure did not completely eliminate the proteins and the resulting product smelt and tasted equally nastily.

The Indians from San Fernando left the expedition at the Island of the Tortoises since they had no experience of naviga-tion through the rapids; and the comparatively large canoe had to be abandoned for one much smaller and infinitely more un-comfortable. It had been hollowed out of a tree trunk with hatchet and fire in the time-honoured manner. With a width of three feet, it just allowed two people to sit side by side. At the stern, lattice-work reaching beyond the gunwale and roofed with leaves, provided some shelter for the four passengers as long as they lay down and stretched their legs out into the sun. The heat under the low roof and the thinness of the hides under-neath turned their accommodation into a veritable martyr's grid. Cages with monkeys and birds, their 'travelling mena-gerie', restricted the space more and more as time went on. Thus they sailed up the Orinoco in a haze of gnats and mos-quitoes. Their camping grounds were the deep layers of rotting leaves of the Amazonian forests; the humid air and massive rains destroyed most of their provisions. For weeks they lived on rice, bananas, ants and an occasional fried monkey, and drank the muddy river water. Every time they wanted to get at their books or equipment, they had to land since the con-stricted space and the instability of the boat made any movement impossible.

In spite of the serious lack of food and the incessant torment of insects, which darkened the air and drove them to camp on islands in the middle of the spray of the cataracts, Humboldt had never been in better health or spirits. He seemed made for the tropics.

The rapids were duly crossed without any serious damage to the boat and they continued their cruise up the Orinoco as far as San Fernando de Atabapo where they entered the Atabapo, a small tributary. Its waters, in contrast to that of the Orinoco which is turbid and smells heavily of dead alligators, are pure and pale yellow in colour. Also, the constant mosquito plague abated there somewhat. Soon they had to leave the river for small streams through the thick forest where an Indian in the bow had to cut a passage through the overhanging boughs with a *machete*. They had now entered the regions of continuous tropical rains; for twelve days and nights, no sun and no stars were visible, to the great detriment of Humboldt's geographical observations. They finally arrived at the mission of Javita, from where their canoe and its cargo had to be carried overland to the Pimichin, a tributary of the Rio Negro, a distance of nine miles. The portage lasted four days, since the poles, on which the boat was dragged along the path, had to be cut on the spot. Every day, Humboldt or Bonpland went along to inspect the work in progress and to make sure that no serious damage had been done. At the end, the bottom of the boat was found to be noticeably thinner but still in one piece. In fact, it survived the whole journey in spite of the hazards of a second crossing of the cataracts. Humboldt, disturbed by the lack of communication along the upper Orinoco and the timeconsuming portage, studied the possibility of a short canal between Atabapo and Pimichin through the forest and even marked the trees along the projected route; the marks may still be recognizable.

Always intent on the economical aspects of newly discovered plants, he used the enforced delay to collect and investigate the native rubber found in the environs. It is formed in lumps on the roots of certain trees and dug out of the marshy ground. The Indians taught him to employ rubber stoppers instead of corks. His travels in the Andes introduced him to seamless rubber boots in Bogotá and to the raincoat in Quito, a thin layer of rubber enclosed between two layers of cloth. Useful as it was, it had the drawback of enveloping the wearer in a strong smell of putrefaction.

Cruising down the Pimichin—all these minor tributaries have still the width of the Thames at Westminster Bridge—they entered the upper Rio Negro, the Guainia, another blackwater river, blessedly free from stinging insects, and embarked at San

Carlos on the exploration of the communication between the Rio Negro, which means finally the Amazon, and the Orinoco. The Jesuit Roman had established on his travels that the Orinoco in its upper course splits into two arms, the Orinoco proper continuing towards the west; and the Casiquiare, which flows to the south and joins the Rio Negro near the little fortress San Carlos guarding the not very distant frontier with Brazil. When La Condamine on his expedition to South America obtained this information from the Jesuits in Para, he communicated it, on his return in 1745, to the Academy of Sciences in Paris, only seven months after the return of Father Roman. The Spanish colonists established in the seventies of the eighteenth century a regular service between Ciudad Bolívar and San Carlos; two or three canoes carried annually salt and the military pay as well as the mail from the lower to the upper Orinoco and the Guainia by way of the Casiquiare. But the European scientists still would not believe in the existence of this singular phenomenon by which two gigantic river systems intercommunicate. La Condamine had admittedly not seen it with his own eyes, and the French geographer Buache persisted in omitting the connection between the Casiquiare and the Orinoco from a map of Guiana published in 1798. He expressed his convictions in a note added to the map: 'the long supposed communication between the Orinoco and the Amazon is a monstrous error in geography which the map of La Cruz has multiplied without foundation; to rectify the ideas entertained on this point, it is only necessary to observe the direction of the great chain of mountains which separates the waters'. Humboldt, by travelling upstream with the Casiquiare to the bifurcation, and up the Orinoco eastwards to Esmeralda and then down the Orinoco again through the rapids and as far as Ciudad Bolívar, proved that this bifurcation or 'inland delta', as he termed it, did in fact exist. He passed the spot where Buache had placed the watershed and could hence demonstrate that the 'great chain of mountains' owed its place on the map entirely to pre-conceived ideas; there simply is no such thing.

The ten-day cruise on the Casiquiare brought back the old torments. With the white water of the river re-appeared the sun, the stars and the mosquitoes. The space on the boat had become even more restricted; they shared it now with seven parrots, eight little monkeys, one dog, a macaw and a toucan. When it came on to rain, the toucan wanted to fish, and the shivery monkeys ran with piteous cries to hide in the long sleeves of Father Zea's habit. Food was scarcer than ever. At San Carlos, the last centre of civilization they had touched, the greatest delicacy offered to them had consisted in smoked ants in a paste of cassava flour tasting of bread-crumbs and rancid butter. Now, they were reduced to the ground-up beans of wild cocoa, followed by draughts of river water. Their progress against the rapid current was slow; they covered about nine miles in fourteen hours of strenuous rowing, shut in by the impenetrable walls of the forest. There was no beach; at night, a space for the camp for about a dozen people had to be hacked out of the jungle. There was no traffic either; for a month, they had met other boats only in the vicinity of the missions. At last they arrived at Esmeralda on the upper Orinoco, a little settle-ment of eighty people under the leadership of an old officer who took the travellers for Catalonian traders on a hopeless and senseless mission. The explanation of their real purpose met with an even greater lack of understanding: why should people come on such a long and arduous journey to survey land in the possession of others. Esmeralda was used as a penal colony; the banishment was dreaded because of the complete isolation and the ferocity of the mosquitoes. Even Father Zea, their fellow traveller from the cataract of the Atures, had to admit that one Esmeraldan mosquito could beat three of the Atures. No priest was in residence there. A friar came five or six times every year from Santa Barbara, a hundred and fifty miles away, to celebrate mass. The officer in charge taught the children the rosary but did not rise to the catechism, and rang the bells for his own amusement.

Esmeralda lies in a plain where wild pineapples grow, at the foot of the mountain group Duida, which Humboldt found to be 8,500 feet high; modern maps give 8,460 feet as the correct figure. The open veins of very fine rock crystal, some of it coloured, in the granite of the rock were thought to be emer' alds and diamonds when the Spaniards first came and named the place. It was one of the sites of the promised land of gold, the 'El Dorado'.

The forests of the upper Orinoco are particularly rich in the tree producing the Brazil nut, a tree which was named *Ber' tholletia excelsa* by Humboldt and Bonpland in honour of the French chemist Berthollet. The harvest of the nuts is the occasion for a festival of dancing and drinking and feasting on broiled monkey. At this time, too, the climbing plants are gathered from which curare is prepared, a poison whose existence had been known since Raleigh but which was first brought to Europe by Humboldt. The travellers were in' structed in the art of distilling curare by the so'called master of poison, an old Indian in charge of the mystery. He preferred the poisoned arrow, since it kills silently, to the European rifle. His hut was transformed into a neat and orderly laboratory with earthenware pots and pans for the distillation and evaporation of the liquid obtained from a cold infusion of the powdered bark, and with funnels made of rolled leaves of the plantain. The cook tasted his broth to decide whether the necessary concentration had been reached; he knew very well that curare becomes only deadly when it is introduced into the blood' stream.

His stay in Esmeralda enabled Humboldt to obtain definite information about the position of the sources of the Orinoco in the mountains east of the mission and to dispose once and for all of the idea of former geographers that the river had its origin on the eastern slopes of the Andes, an error occasioned by the confusion of the Orinoco with its mighty tributaries—and also by the fact that it doubles back on its course, so that after flowing along a distance of 1,560 miles, it is only 346 miles from its source, measured in a direct line.

In 1958, the botanists Volkmar Vareschi, and Karl Mägde-frau, repeated Humboldt's Orinoco journey in a canoe which had been provided with an outboard motor. They did the whole circuit in thirty-nine days instead of Humboldt's forty-one. Many of the settlements described by him have been abandoned and no trace exists of Esmeralda although it is still to be found on every modern map. The Indian tribes are un-changed in their habits, and mosquitoes, ants and wasps are the undisputed masters of the river territory.

The journey back was much more easily accomplished. Humboldt and Bonpland spent many nights on the boat, let-ting it drift downstream in the middle of the current where the mosquitoes were not quite so plentiful. After a cruise of 1,500 miles, they arrived in Ciudad Bolívar, the town by the straits, on the 15th of June 1800. After their long stay in the wilderness, this small country town with not more than 6,000 inhabitants appeared to them as the peak of civilization. The stay in Ciu-dad Bolívar had to be prolonged for a month; both Humboldt and Bonpland had to pay for their journey through the interior by a serious attack of fever in which Humboldt had the oppor-tunity to experience the curative powers of *cortex Angosturae*, the basic ingredient of Angostura bitters. At last, they reached the coast again, where, at Cumana, Bonpland caused a new delay. This time he did not fall ill but in love—with an Indian girl with whom he ran off into the surrounding forest. At last, in November, when Humboldt had nearly given up the hope of seeing him again, he returned from his adventure and they set sail for Havana.

At this time they had planned to explore the west coast of North America as far as Canada, to go south to the Missis-sippi—the greater part of whose course was still unknown—

and to sail eventually from Mexico to the Philippines, then also in the possession of the Spanish crown. But when they saw an American newspaper report that Baudin with his expedition was on his way round Cape Horn to the coast of Peru, Humboldt decided to join them in Lima. He was always the guiding spirit; true, he financed the exploration, but he was also much the more purposeful of the two. Bonpland, as his subsequent career proved, preferred a less active existence.

Some of the time spent in Cuba was devoted to the disposal of their collections. The war at sea made communication with Europe very precarious at that time. Only one letter out of four sent overseas reached its destination, for the captains of the mailboats were inclined to jettison their mailbags at the mere sight of a British ship. Since his departure from Spain, Humboldt had received just five or six letters in the two years of his absence. He had made it his practice to send one letter only on every occasion and to repeat his information several times. In the same way he dispersed now his collections of plants which had been sadly depleted by the ravages of the humid climate and the attacks of innumerable insects. They kept one small herbarium for their personal use; a second was sent off to France and a third to London. The descriptions of the plants, 1,400 new or rare species, were likewise duplicated. Very few of the cases sent off during the expedition reached their destination. Years later, a collection of rock specimens from the Andes, which had been captured by a British ship, came into the hands of Sir Joseph Banks, who offered to return them to Humboldt.

Five

THE ANDES AND MEXICO

AFTER the plains and forests of Venezuela, after the hydro-graphical exploration of its immense river system, Humboldt and Bonpland turned now to the volcanic mountain range of the Andes, one of the highest and most imposing of the world. The results revolutionized the geological views of the time; Werner's neptunism was finally superseded by the concept of the volcanic origin of granite and gneiss and of the existence of geological faults, deep clefts along which the earth's crust changes its formation. They spent nearly two years in Colom-bia, Ecuador and Peru, crossing the various ranges by their highest passes and climbing a number of the peaks. They started their trek from Cartagena with a visit to the forests and gas volcanoes of Turbaco.

'In the centre of a vast plain bordered by pineapple plants, arise eighteen to twenty little cones, twenty to twenty-five feet high. These cones are of a blackish-grey clay with an opening at the top which is filled with water. At the approach to the little craters, a dull and fairly strong noise can be heard which precedes at fifteen to eighteen seconds intervals the release of a great quantity of air. The force with which this air rises above the surface of the water leads me to suppose that it is exposed to great pressure in the interior of the earth. I counted in general five explosions in two minutes. The phenomenon is often accompanied by an ejection of mud. The Indians assured us that the cones had not noticeably changed their shape in many years; but the force and frequency of the explosions seem to show a variation with the seasons. I found by a chemical analysis that the released air contains less than five per cent of

II. Natural bridge of Icononzo over the Rio de la Suma Paz (Colombia), from 'Sites in the Cordilleras', after a sketch by Alexander von Humboldt

oxygen. It is a pure nitrogen, purer than that normally prepared in our laboratories.'[1]

The quickest route to Lima, where Humboldt hoped to meet Baudin, would have been by sea, but the road by land across the Andes offered the possibility of mapping the country north of the Amazon. Added to that, there was the attraction of meeting the botanist Mutis in Bogotá who had been a friend of Linnaeus and who was a great authority on South American plants. The first part of the journey led up the Magdalena river between sparsely inhabited forests. The river was in full spate and the rapid current made their progress slow. Gales and thunderstorms continued uninterruptedly. In all these discomforts, Humboldt kept up his geographical determinations and the observations of meteorological data. After a cruise of forty-five days, in which they had covered a distance of about three hundred miles, they landed at the town of Honda in Colombia, and reached the plain round Bogotá, after a climb which had taken them up steps cut into the rock and not more than twenty inches wide where the pack mules could scarcely push through. This road to Bogotá, then a town of about thirty thousand inhabitants, remained in the state described by Humboldt until the Spaniards had regained possession of the district during the civil wars in 1816. It was then that the Spanish government set Republican prisoners to widen and improve the road for military reasons where for three hundred years only a wretched path had existed.

Their arrival in Bogotá had been expected; the archbishop had sent his carriage and they entered the town in a triumphal procession as the distinguished visitors of the highly respected Mutis whose collections and library were put at Humboldt's and Bonpland's disposal. Here, as everywhere in Spanish America, they were welcomed as if the seclusion of the Spanish colonies had never existed. There were no social barriers either; even the viceroy entertained them to lunch at his country seat (he was forbidden by etiquette to eat with lesser mortals in his town residence).

To reach Quito, the route over Quindiu was chosen, difficult and strenuous but more interesting than the path through the valleys. From September 1801 until their descent to Trujillo in October 1802, Humboldt and Bonpland stayed on the highland of the Andes, crossing and re-crossing the Cordilleras. Their investigations of the high peaks turned them into the finest mountaineers of their time; Humboldt's climb of Chimborazo to the height of 19,280 feet remained a world record for nearly thirty years. The Cordilleras form three ranges, of which that at Bogotá is the most easterly, and both the central and the western chains had to be surmounted to reach the coasts of the Pacific. Draught oxen carried the baggage. Humboldt and Bonpland travelled on foot, as they refused to follow the degrading custom of the country and allow them-selves to be carried by human beasts of burden, the so-called Cargueros. These men tied a chair to their backs for the traveller to sit on and marched with their passenger for three to four hours a day. They earned only a few shillings a week, but it was their only livelihood, and they strenuously objected to the plans of the provincial governor to build a proper road.

Away from the towns, the regions of the Andes are desolate. The route led through the forests and swamps on the slopes, where the mules and oxen sank into the ground and the boots perished on the travellers' feet, to the high plateaux, the scarcely inhabited Paramos. At an elevation of over ten thousand feet, under a cold and grey sky, the abundant equatorial vegetation is replaced by low, myrtle-like shrubs and alpine herbs and flowers which flourish in the damp mountain mists. At night, the Indians put up their tents: wooden poles, cut in the forests, provided the supports and the large leaves of a palm tree, overlapping each other like tiles, formed the covering. Their waxy surface keeps them water-tight. In the morning, the leaves

are rolled up like umbrellas, the poles dismantled and every/
thing is transported to the next camp. From Popayán onwards,
the evidence of volcanic activities and violent earthquakes was
everywhere around them. For over a year, from November
1801 until their departure to Mexico in January 1803, Hum/
boldt made investigations of the geological structure of these
regions, of the gas content of the volcanic exhalations, the pro/
pagation of seismic waves and the composition of the atmo/
sphere at heights up to 19,000 feet. He discovered that the
whole high/lying part of the province of Quito forms one
single volcanic system, of which the volcanoes of Cotopaxi and
Pichincha act as the vents of their common focus. Only five
years earlier, in 1797, the town of Riobamba, south of Quito,
had been destroyed in a severe earthquake with the loss of
40,000 lives; and the ground still trembled occasionally. Even
the climate had taken a turn for the worse; the mean tempera/
ture had gone down and the sky was usually grey and mourn/
ful. The people of Quito, determined to enjoy the moment,
gaily danced on their volcano; vivacious and charming, they
had created a sophisticated life and beautiful surroundings on
very insecure foundations.

Every one of the volcanoes on the plateau was climbed by
Humboldt, sometimes alone, sometimes accompanied by
Bonpland. Their Indian guides, who had not much experience
of the terrain, were frightened and inclined to desert from the
insensate undertaking.

'Twice, on the 26th and the 28th of May (1802), I climbed
to the crater of Pichincha which rises above Quito. Nobody
but Condamine had seen it before me as far as I know and he
did not reach it until he had lost five or six days in a futile
search. He arrived without instruments and could not endure
the cold for more than fifteen minutes. I succeeded in taking
my instruments with me, I managed to carry out the more im/
portant observations and to collect some air for analysis. The
first journey I made alone with one Indian. Since Condamine

had approached the crater from the snow-covered side of the rim, I followed the first time in his footsteps. That was nearly the end of us. The Indian sank up to his chest into a crevasse and we discovered to our horror that we had passed over a bridge of iced snow. A few steps away, we could see daylight through the holes. Without realising it, we had stood on vaults overhanging the crater. Frightened but undeterred, I decided on a different approach. Three rocky peaks stretching out over the abyss rise from the circumference of the crater; they are free of snow since it is melted by the steam from the opening of the volcano. I climbed one of these peaks and discovered at the top a stone which, supported only on one side, formed a kind of balcony above the abyss. Here, I established myself with my instruments. This stone is about twelve feet long and six feet wide and is shaken by frequent earth tremors; we counted eighteen in not quite thirty minutes. We lay down flat to get a better look at the bottom of the crater; nobody can imagine anything more sinister, mournful and deathly than what we saw there. The gorge of the volcano forms a circular hole of about one mile in circumference; the broken edge is covered with snow and the interior a dull black in colour. But the depth is so enormous that it contains several mountains whose peaks can be just discovered. They seemed to be perhaps 1,900 feet below us. How far down can it be to the bottom? I believe that the bottom of the crater lies at the same height as the town of Quito. La Condamine found the crater extinct and covered with snow. We were forced to tell the people the sad news that their nearby volcano is on fire. The unmistakable signs did not leave any doubts. We were nearly suffocated by sulphurous vapours at the approach to the opening. We saw bluish flames flicker in the depths and felt violent tremors every two or three minutes. They shook the rim of the crater but became unnoticeable at a distance of two hundred yards. It seems that the catastrophe of 1797 has relighted the fires of Pichincha.'[2]

On the 9th of June 1802, Humboldt and Bonpland, accom⁄
panied by the son of the provincial governor, made their
record⁄breaking attempt to climb Chimborazo. At a height of
19,170 feet they were stopped by a large fissure which made any
further ascent impossible. Separated from the summit by only
thirteen hundred feet, they had to turn back after a barometric
determination of the height and after collecting samples of air.
They were all suffering from mountain sickness which per⁄
sisted for days after, even in the plain, a sickness which Hum⁄
boldt ascribed to the effects of the low oxygen content of the
atmosphere at these elevations. The weathered lava streams,
mixed with pumice stone, over which they had climbed,
betrayed the volcanic origin of this Andean colossus. Hum⁄
boldt was at that time firmly convinced that he had been
on the highest mountain of the world; and he had not even
been on the highest peak in South America. The elevation of
the Himalayas was not determined until a quarter of a century
later. Humboldt had to admit to a twinge of annoyance when
Boussingault in the course of his South American travels
reached a height of 19,700 feet on Chimborazo in 1831. After
more than thirty years, he was dethroned from his mountaineer⁄
ing eminence.

After a whole year's travel along the crest of the Andes,
Humboldt and Bonpland descended gradually through the
milder climate of the cinchona woods on the slopes to the
upper Amazon. The impressions of wilderness and desolation
of the scarcely inhabited regions with their all but impassable
paths were heightened by the sight of the old roads of the Incas.
With their deep understructure and pavement of porphyry
blocks, they appeared superior even to the Roman roads Hum⁄
boldt had seen in Italy, France and Spain. The architectural
remains of the Peruvian civilization enhanced the fascination
of the country in Humboldt's eyes. For the European mind, the
visual reminders of the past with their appeal to the historical
sense give an added depth to the enjoyment of the natural

scene. In the Orinoco basin, the Indian languages are the only sources of the traditions and beliefs of the original population of the country, and Humboldt had collected information on the structure and vocabularies of the various Indian tribes, on their legends and mythologies. Quechua, the language of the Incas, was then commonly used even by the Spanish upper classes for its subtlety and flexibility. The search for archae⁄ological and historical remains of the pre⁄conquest civilizations had produced an unexpected harvest in Riobamba: Humboldt was given occasion to study memoirs, written in the sixteenth century, of the events preceding the conquest of the province of Quito by the Incas. A descendant of the Inca kings was in possession of these manuscripts, which had been written by one of his ancestors in a now extinct dialect and later translated into Spanish by another member of the same family. In addi⁄tion to previously unknown information on the structure of this state, Humboldt was delighted to discover a description of the eruption of the Altar, at that time probably the highest peak in that region. The explosion carried away part of the summit; the reports say that the eruption lasted for seven years and the volcanic ashes fell so frequently and densely that for seven years the neighbouring towns were in perpetual darkness.

The way down the slopes of the Andes to Jaen led back to tropical forests with groves of purplish⁄pink Bougainvillaeas and cinchona trees, a source of quinine. The total output of the drug, which was inconsiderable compared with the natural occurrence of the plant, was at that time reserved for the Spanish court. In a short exploration of the sources of the Amazon, Humboldt came upon a singular and idyllic mail route. A 'water courier', usually a young Indian, regularly carried the post by swimming down the Huancabamba, a tributary of the Amazon, to its junction with this river. At the rapids, he left the water and made a detour through the woods. Sometimes, he took a friend to keep him company on his two days' journey, from which he returned by a much longer and more laborious route over the mountain passes. The letters, hidden under a cotton turban, arrived quite dry; only very rarely, in sudden floods, did they happen to be lost. A number of the Indian tribes on the banks of the upper Amazon were in the habit of travelling in this way; large sociable parties of thirty to forty persons, men, women and children, could be seen swimming down river.

Turning back from the tropical regions, Humboldt and his companions recrossed the Andes near Cajamarca at a point where the inclination of the magnetic compass passes from the north to the south. They had traversed the magnetic equator. Humboldt's determination of the magnetic intensity at this spot served as reference point for all geomagnetic measurements of the next fifty years. At last, at the highest position on the seaward descent, they saw for the first time the Pacific Ocean; in their excitement, they forgot to determine the height of the pass. This view had a particular meaning for Humboldt; he had seen the sea of Captain Cook's travels, of which he had heard Forster's vivid personal descriptions. A successful observation of a transit of Mercury enabled him to make an accurate determination of the longitude of Callao and the coastal passage from Lima to Guayaquil gave him the opportunity to measure the temperature and course of the famous cold current which bears his name. On his own maps, it is always called 'Peruvian current'. He strongly objected to the designation 'Humboldt current'. The current had been known for the last three hundred years to every fisherman from Chile to Payta; his only merit was to have measured the temperature of the water for the first time.

The travellers set sail in Guayaquil and arrived at Acapulco in March 1803, to spend the last year of their expedition in Mexico. Cotopaxi was in eruption and its thunder was audible on the boat nearly two hundred miles away.

Mexico was of course a developed and prosperous country, and the stay there did not lead to new geographical discoveries

but to a thorough geological, geographical and political investigation. All the volcanoes were climbed again in turn, the
silver mines visited, and a great many determinations of latitudes and longitudes carried out. Humboldt and Bonpland
had the singular experience of seeing a comparatively recently
formed volcano, the Jorullo. 'The volcano Jorullo lies according to my observations at 19° 9' latitude and 103° 51' 48"
longitude, west of the city of Mexico. It rises 1,683 feet above
the neighbouring plains. Its height is therefore three times
that of the Monte Nuovo at Pozzuoli which arose in 1528. It is
surrounded by thousands of small basaltic cones. This enormous upthrust took place in the night of the 29th of September 1759. The former level of the overthrown terrain is now
called the *malpays*. Broken strata separate it from the undisturbed part of the plain. Extending over four square miles, it is
broken up by small cones, six to nine feet high. The raised
ground has the shape of a bubble whose convexity increases
progressively towards the centre, so that at the foot of the great
volcano the ground is 525 feet above the Indian huts in the
plain where we stayed.'

'The cones are so many fumaroles emitting a dense vapour
which makes the surrounding air unbearably hot. They are
called in this extremely unhealthy district *hornitos* or little ovens.
A shell of hard clay encloses spheres of basalt. Ashes cover the
slopes of the great volcano which is still on fire. We reached the
interior of the crater by clambering over a hill of hard scoria-
ceous lava which rises to a considerable height. All Mexican
volcanoes lie arranged along an east–west line which forms at
the same time a parallel of latitude of the great peaks. When we
consider this fact and compare it with the observations on the
boche nuove of Vesuvius, we are tempted to believe that the
subterranean fire has forced an opening through an enormous
crevice which exists in the interior of the earth at a latitude of
18° 59' to 19° 12' and which stretches from the Pacific to the
Atlantic Ocean.'[3]

This account has an added piquancy today: on the 20th of February 1943, a new volcano, Paricutín, began to erupt north-west of Jorullo. It has now reached a height of 1,000 feet.

After a short second stay in Cuba, Humboldt and Bonpland sailed for Philadelphia where they arrived in May 1804. The results of their observations were not unknown in the world since those of his letters which arrived in Europe had been read in meetings of the *Institut* in Paris and published in French and German newspapers. Humboldt's unique knowledge of South American conditions and his research into the economics and geography of Mexico had resulted in an offer from the Mexican government of a ministerial post. He had refused, since it was his firm intention to maintain an independence which gave him the freedom to express his opinions even if they did not conform to current political ideas. He was deeply interested in the new North American republic and paid his respects to Jefferson, her president, immediately on landing. Jefferson replied by an invitation to Monticello, his residence.

Washington, May 28th, 1804.
SIR!

I received last night your favor of the 24th and offer you my congratulations on your arrival here in good health after a tour in the course of which you have been exposed to so many hardships and hazards. The countries you have visited are of those least known and most interesting, and a lively desire will be felt generally to receive the information you will be able to give. No one will feel it more strongly than myself, because no one perhaps views this new world with more partial hopes of its exhibiting an ameliorated state of the human condition. In the new position in which the seat of the government is fixed, we have nothing curious to attract the observation of a traveller, and can only substitute in its place the welcome with which we should receive your visit, should you find it convenient to add so much to your journey. Accept, I pray you, my respectful salutations and assurances of great respect and consideration etc.

JEFFERSON.[4]

The stay lasted for three weeks. Humboldt reported many years after that Jefferson discussed with him his ideas about the political future of America, 'the project of a future division of the American continent into three great republics which were to include Mexico and the South American states which at that time belonged to the Spanish crown'.

After a sea passage of twenty-five days, they docked in Bordeaux on the 3rd of August 1804. Any plan of a visit to the Philippines had been abandoned when Humboldt discovered the impossibility of obtaining replacements from Europe for his worn-out instruments. He had been provided with an eight-inch Hadley sextant by Ramsden with a silver circle graduated at twenty-second intervals and a two-inch Troughton sextant, a kind of pocket edition which he called his snuffbox sextant. It was extremely accurate and very convenient to carry in difficult terrain. His barometers and thermometers had been standardized before his departure with those of the Paris observatory. The longitude determinations were made with a Dollond telescope and a chronometer by Berthoud whose rate of variation had been carefully checked. Three different kinds of electrometer, provided with pith spheres, straws and gold-leaf, allowed him to observe atmospheric electricity. He also possessed a Dollond balance for the measurements of the specific gravity of sea water, an eudiometer for the analysis of atmospheric gases, a Leyden jar and the necessary chemicals and glass bottles as well as a cyanometer designed by Saussure. This was an instrument by which the blueness of the sky could be determined through comparison with prepared gradations of blue colours and correlated with the hygrometrically determined humidity. The magnetic measurements were carried out with a Borda magnetometer, a rather cumbersome instrument. It consisted of a horizontal divided circle of about twenty inches diameter on which a vertical divided circle could be rotated, and with it a magnetic needle of the length of one foot, pivoted on a steel axis. The intensity of the earth's magnetic field was determined from the period of oscillation with reference to that obtaining at Paris. Humboldt had two such magnets in his possession, one of which had been magnetized before his departure; he kept them in oiled paper and they retained their polish undiminished in spite of the tropical climate. Their magnetization was checked on his return. On sea, the instrument was suspended on a long thread in a Cardani suspension near the poop of the ship, as far away as possible from iron parts. In all, one hundred and twenty-four magnetic observations were made in the course of the journey.

The arrival of the party was greeted in Bordeaux with the liveliest surprise since the news of their death from yellow fever had preceded them from Philadelphia. One of Humboldt's first preoccupations was with the state of his finances. He was a good political economist but very improvident with his own money. In the rather pathetic account he kept in his travel diary he calculated in 1802 that the journey would cost him about eleven hundred pounds of his capital, of which he hoped to recover seven hundred pounds from publications. In Mexico, he enters: 'I thought to-day that until my return to Europe I shall have swallowed sixteen hundred pounds of my capital, exclusive of what I may earn by writing. In 1804, I shall probably have a capital of fifteen thousand pounds.' A little later, he came to the conclusion that until the end of 1803 his journey would have cost him over four thousand pounds; the account sent to him by his old tutor Kunth after his return to France disclosed that his inheritance of seventeen thousand pounds had now shrunk to eleven thousand six hundred pounds and that his income had fallen from six hundred and sixty pounds in 1797 to five hundred and sixty pounds in 1804.

They returned to a France transformed from a revolutionary republic into the domain of an emperor who received Humboldt with very moderate enthusiasm. All he found to say to him was: 'You are interested in botany? So is my wife,' before he turned away. The members of the *Institut* however—they had elected Humboldt a corresponding member in the preceding February—organized a meeting at which he was given the opportunity to outline the scientific results of his investigations.

'My cherished and ardent desire has been fulfilled. In the dense forests of the Rio Negro, surrounded by jaguars and ferocious crocodiles, tormented by the stings of mosquitoes and ants, for three months no food other than water, bananas and fish, among the Otomac Indians who live on clay, or on the banks of the Casiquiare where within three hundred miles no human being is to be found, in these unpleasant situations I never regretted my plans. The discomforts have been very great but only momentary.

'I aim at collecting ideas rather than material objects. A private person who with moderate means undertakes a journey round the world, has to confine himself to matters of major interest. To study the formation of the earth and its strata, to analyse the atmosphere, to measure with sensitive instruments its pressure, temperature, humidity, the electric and magnetic charge, to observe the influence of the climate on the distribution of plants and animals, to relate chemistry to the physiology of organized beings, these are the aims I have proposed to myself.'

Humboldt's means may have been moderate, his aims certainly were not. Yet the results of his expedition justified his assertions. The exploration of the Casiquiare and the upper Orinoco settled an outstanding geographical problem; the knowledge of the structure of the Andes and the placement of their volcanoes opened a new chapter to the geologist. Meteorology was provided with a great mass of much-needed data and the subject of plant geography came into being. Oceanography, was enriched by a knowledge of the temperature and velocity of currents, and, last but not least, the observations on the geomagnetic field led Gauss to his formulation of the theory of magnetic fields. In the field of archaeology, we are indebted to Humboldt for his interest in Indian languages and the remains of their civilizations.

III. Rope bridge of Penipé over Rio Chambo (Ecuador), from 'Sites in the Cordilleras', after a sketch by Alexander von Humboldt

With his arrival in France begins a different but equally intense activity; the next twenty years were spent in the publication of his great work on South America and a continuation of his experimental research which, among other results, led to the discovery of magnetic storms.

Six

THE GEOMAGNETIC FIELD AND
MAGNETIC STORMS

FROM 1804 until 1827, Humboldt lived in the main in Paris. It was probably the happiest period in his life in spite of the political uproar, from the collapse of the Prussian state after the battle of Jena to the Congress of Vienna and its long aftermath. In Paris he found the scientific collaborators and the libraries he needed to collate the results of his expedition and to carry out the experimental research demanded by the data he had col-lected. There also he found the engravers to draw his maps and illustrations and the publishers willing and able to undertake the publication of his great work.

Napoleon's imperial lavishness extended to scientific institu-tions as much as to official buildings, art collections and a luxuriant court life. An enumeration of the scientists then working in Paris becomes a wearying list of names still on the lips of every scientist. The work of the humanists was of equal importance in a period when the foundations of modern philology were laid. Artists and writers leavened the life of a society in which politicians met intellectuals and artists. The great chemist Berthollet and later the painter Gérard, a pupil of David, were in the habit of collecting men and women of very varied attainments in their houses. They were all people for whom a many-sided conversation provided the mental vita-mins necessary to stimulate their minds; as with vitamins, the effect seems out of all proportion to the small doses needed. Out of Berthollet's parties at his house in Arcueil, near Paris, grew a scientific society, the Société d'Arcueil, and a scientific journal, the *Mémoires de la Société d'Arcueil*. The French scientists and mathematicians of this period were undoubtedly much more brilliant in their field than the writers and artists. The formation of 'schools', of circles of young men round the great authorities, with whom to discuss the latest data and the more untractable problems of the day, is the best guarantee for continuity of achievement. The century of experimental science was also a century of theory *par excellence*. The accumulation of new data demanded a new insight into the causal nexus and new mathematical methods for an exact representation; the collaboration between experimentalists and theorists was extremely close. Science has its artists and its craftsmen; it is the artist to whom a personal exchange of ideas and an atmosphere of discussion is vital. Their period lasted well into our century. The occurrence of so many outstanding intellects was quite divorced from even approximately appropriate financial rewards; the emoluments of an academic position were wretched to the point of penury, at any rate on the continent. It was, and partly still is, the tacit assumption that only a man with private means could afford such a career; anybody else who was stubborn enough to attempt it, had to take the consequences. The number of wealthy amateurs like Cavendish or Humboldt, men who never competed for official positions, was fairly small. The majority were without financial backing; they had to supplement their unsatisfactory salaries by doing work as external examiners, writing articles, or holding a second post, in short, by all the ways and means well known today (apart from radio and television). Out of the money thus acquired, an experimenter had to provide his own laboratory equipment. In spite of these difficulties, there was no shortage of truly brilliant minds. Patronage, wherever it may come from, can attract indifferent talents but it cannot create the burning interest and quiet obsession which will produce completely new ideas. The number of craftsmen can be enlarged; the number of artists is still in the lap of the gods.

Very soon after his return to Europe, Humboldt became a

regular guest at Berthollet's scientific gatherings; here he met the young chemist Gay-Lussac whose very unfavourable criti-cism of Humboldt's early work on the composition of air had attracted his notice. Humboldt's approach to Gay-Lussac, frank and without rancour, led to a very close friendship; they continued these experiments together. Their main concern was the determination of the oxygen content of air from various sources and at varying heights above the ground. Gay-Lussac, in collaboration with Biot, had already made use of balloons for this purpose, in which they had ascended to over twenty-three thousand feet. They collected air in damp and dry weather, in gales from all directions of the compass, and even air from the Théâtre Français, taken at the beginning, middle and end of a performance. They discovered that the oxygen content of the atmosphere remains unchanged at 21 per cent of the volume within a limit of accuracy of 0·1 per cent. Their experimental method was based on Cavendish's discovery that a mixture of hydrogen and oxygen combines to form water when an electric spark is passed through it. They added a known volume of hydrogen to a known volume of air, sent an electric spark through it, and measured the change in the volume of gas; the decrease gave the amount of oxygen which had been used up in the combination to water. They went carefully into the problem whether the admixture of other gases had any influence on the completeness with which the hydrogen present was burned. The experiments were the occasion for a very im-portant discovery: in all circumstances, two parts of hydrogen combine with one part of oxygen to form one part of water. This statement is the basis of the modern concept of chemical valencies. Humboldt himself said later in his life: 'Berzelius has reported that this fact is the germ of the subsequent dis-coveries on fixed proportions but this discernment of complete saturation is entirely due to Gay-Lussac's sagacity. I colla-borated in this part of the experiments but he alone saw the theoretical importance of the result.'[1]

In the spring of the year 1805, the two friends set out on a journey over the Alps into Italy, armed with magnetic instruments and equipment for gas analysis, to continue their investigations into the composition of air and to extend Humboldt's measurements of the geomagnetic intensity at different latitudes in continuation of the very important work done on the South American expedition.

The use of the magnetic compass had very early on led to a knowledge of the variation with geographical position of the magnetic declination, the deviation of the magnetic needle from the true north. Halley's world map of the magnetic declinations had been published in 1702; it had been followed in 1768 by Wilcke's map of the lines of equal magnetic dip, i.e. the angle between the horizontal and the position of the magnetic needle. The geographical distribution of the intensity on the earth was, however, unknown at the time of Humboldt's expedition to South America.

Mallet, in 1769, had been the first to attempt the measurement of the magnetic intensity at different latitudes; his instrument, through lack of sensitivity, gave the erroneous result of a constant magnetic field over a range of seven degrees of latitude. Thus, the idea arose that the geomagnetic field is constant over the whole surface of the earth, an idea which found even Cavendish's support. Borda, who, on theoretical grounds, did not share this opinion, repeated the experiment with a dip magnetometer of his own design on his journey to Senegambia in 1776 but discovered that the friction of the magnet on the pivots prevented the attainment of the necessary sensitivity. On his return to Paris, he improved the construction of his instrument; on his advice and provided with the improved inclination magnetometer, Humboldt carried out his measurements in South America. He made 124 observations over a range of longitudes of 115° and over latitudes between 52° N and 12° S; at every point, he measured the geographical position of the locality, its height above sea level, and noted the distance from the mountains and the composition of neighbouring rocks, well aware of the influence of these factors on magnetic data. As the unit of field strength he chose the period of oscillation at a point in Peru where the magnetic inclination vanishes. This unit remained in general use well into the 1850's, long after the establishment of the absolute unit which is now called a *gauss*. The results were published in 1804 in the form of zones of equal magnetic strength, the so-called isodynamic zones, since the relatively small number of observations did not permit a representation in isodynamic lines. There were four such zones north of the geographical equator and one to the south. In the same year, Gay-Lussac had proved in a balloon ascent which reached the height of 21,600 feet, that the magnetic field of the earth extended into the upper atmosphere, and Biot had tried to account for the geographical variation of the dip. He assumed that the origin of the earth's field is a small magnetic dipole with its centre in the centre of the spherical earth and its axis perpendicular to the magnetic equator. This hypothesis results in lines of equal dip running parallel to the magnetic equator, contrary to experience; also, the increase of the intensity from equator to poles does not follow the observed data. The terms 'isogonics', 'isoclines' and 'isodynamics' for the lines of equal declination, inclination and intensity were coined by Humboldt; they are now generally accepted expressions.

The variation of the magnetic intensity with geographical latitude had been observed before Humboldt but the importance of these results had been overlooked, and the fact itself forgotten. Humboldt himself has given an account of the history of this discovery.

The following is the history of the discovery of the law of the increase of the force with the magnetic latitude. When I intended to join the expedition of Captain Baudin round the world in 1798, I was asked by Borda, who took a warm interest in the execution of my projects, to observe in both hemispheres at different latitudes the oscillations of a perpendicular needle in the magnetic meridian in order to find out if the intensity of the force is constant or variable. On my journey to the American tropics, I made this investigation one of the main tasks of my undertaking. I observed that the same needle which in Paris showed in ten minutes 245 oscillations, in Havana 246, in Mexico 242, underwent within the same time 216 at San Carlos del Rio Negro (latitude 1° 53′ N, longitude 80° 40′ W), on the magnetic equator, i.e. the line where the inclination is zero, in Peru (latitude 7° 1′ S, longitude 80° 40′ W), only 211, in Lima (latitude 12° 2′ S) again 219 oscillations. I observed therefore in the years 1799 to 1803 that the total intensity if it is set equal to one on the magnetic equator in the Peruvian Andes between Micui‑pampa and Cajamarca, can be expressed as 1·3482 in Paris, in Mexico as 1·3155, in San Carlos as 1·0480, in Lima as 1·0773. When I developed at the meeting of the Paris *Institut* of the 26th Frimaire of the year XIII this law of the variable intensity of the terrestrial magnetic force in a treatise for whose mathematical part Mr. Biot is responsible, and when I proved it by numerical observations in 104 different localities, the fact was considered to be completely new. Only *after* this paper had been read, as Biot has very decidedly said, did de Rossel communicate to Biot his six *earlier* observations of oscillations which had been made from 1791 to 1794 in Van Diemen Land, Java and Amboina. They equally proved the law of decreasing force in the Indian archipelago. It seems not unlikely that this excellent man had not recognised in his own work the regular decrease and increase of the intensity since he had never said anything to our common friends Laplace, Delambre, Prony and Biot about this, surely not unimportant, physical law before the reading of my paper. His observations were not published until 1808, four years after my return from America. Until the present day, it has been the custom in all the tables of magnetic intensity which have been published in Ger‑many, England and France, to reduce the observed oscillations to that unit of force which I discovered on the magnetic equator in northern Peru: with this arbitrary unit, the magnetic force becomes 1·348 in Paris. Still older however than the observations of Admiral Rossel are those, made by Lamanon during the expedition of the unfortunate Lapérouse from his stay in Tenerife (1785) to the arrival in Macao (1787), and forwarded to the academy of sciences. It is certain that they were in the hands of Condorcet in July, 1787; in spite of all efforts, they have not been found again. Captain Duperrey possesses a copy of a very important letter by Lamanon to the perpetual secretary of the academy of that time which has been omitted from the *Voyage de Lapérouse*. It is said there expressly that the attractive force of the magnet is less in the tropics than towards the poles and that the intensity derived from the number of oscillations of the inclination compass changes and increases with latitude. If the academy of sciences had felt justified to publish in 1787, before the hoped-for return of the unfortunate Lapérouse, a truth which has been discovered by three travellers, none of whom knew the other, the theory of geomagnetism would have been enlarged eighteen years earlier by a new class of phenomena. This simple account of the facts can perhaps justify an assertion contained in the third volume of my *Relation historique* (p. 615): The observations on the variations of terrestrial magnetism which I have carried out during a period of thirty-two years in America, Europe and Asia and with comparable instruments, cover in both hemispheres, from the frontiers of Chinese Dzungaria to the Pacific Ocean which bathes the coasts of Mexico and Peru, a space of 188° of longitude, from 60° northern lattiude to 12° S. I have considered the law of the decrease of the magnetic forces from the pole to the equator as the most important result of my American journey. It is not certain but very likely that Lamanon's letter of July 1787 was read by Condorcet at a meeting of the academy of sciences in Paris; I consider such a reading a completely valid form of publication. The first recognition of the law therefore belongs incontestably to the companion of Lapérouse; but long unnoticed or forgotten, the knowledge of the variation of magnetic intensity with latitude has only gained life, or so I believe, with the publication of my observations of 1799 to 1804. The object and the length of this note will not astonish those who are familiar with the more recent history of magetism and the doubts to which it has given rise, and who know from their own experience that some value is attached to the work of five years, carried out under the difficulties of the tropical climate and hazardous mountain travel. [2]

For their magnetic observations on the Italian journey, Humboldt and Gay-Lussac timed the oscillations of a declination magnetometer, a procedure which is less cumbersome. A similar instrument served Humboldt on his expedition to Russia and on his various excursions to the Bohemian spas.

The two travellers crossed the Alps, on foot, over the St. Bernard Pass; they had even taken a balloon with which they had hoped to study the air currents at low heights above the mountains, but continuous fogs prevented them from using it. In Bologna they visited Count Zambeccari, a martyr of science. Engaged in similar experiments, he had made several balloon ascents. At his last attempt, the balloon burst into flames over his head and he had to slide down the safety rope to save himself; he lost six fingers as a result. He was still in bed when Humboldt saw him, but sufficiently recovered to discuss with Gay-Lussac the project of a hydrogen-filled balloon under which he meant to arrange a circle of lamps which could be lighted and extinguished to control the height of ascent. As Humboldt said: 'This time he will blow himself up instead of burning himself.' And eventually he did, too.

Seven weeks after leaving Paris, they arrived in Rome, where Wilhelm Humboldt was at that time Prussian envoy at the Vatican. His main professional duties consisted in obtaining divorces for the Roman Catholic members of the Prussian aristocracy (or so his brother said). For the rest, he and his very gifted wife kept open house for foreign artists, and Wilhelm devoted himself to his studies of languages. 'My brother's house was more animated than ever since at that time Mme. de Stael delighted the eternal city and the great artists Thorvaldsen and Rauch came every day and Leopold von Buch stayed there; Gay-Lussac, launched into a world composed of so diverse elements, adapted himself very well to it since he had a lively feeling for nature and the arts whose charms had been relatively unknown to him until then.'[3]

A sudden eruption of Vesuvius gave them occasion for a series of observations on the height of the crater and the behaviour of the local geomagnetic field during a volcanic upheaval; it was found that no variations occurred. Humboldt used his stay in Italy to search through the Mexican codices in Italian libraries for his work on pre-conquest civilization in Mexico. Continuing their experiments, they returned over the Alps to Germany where Humboldt was received with the honours due to him. A medal was struck to commemorate his expedition and he gave a lecture at a special meeting of the Berlin Academy of Sciences whose member he had become. He made at the same time some proposals for the reform of this somewhat somnolent institution, of which he had said that it reminded him of a hospital where the patients slept better than the healthy.

He had started on the publication of the material he had collected in South America, in particular the account of the geography and economics of Mexico, for which Humboldt expected some success in England. At that time, an English mission had been sent to Berlin in an attempt to organize an alliance against Napoleon, and Humboldt was trying to interest them in his work.

I have become great friends with Lord Harrowby, Mr. Hammond and Lord Gower, Mr. Pierpoint and the whole diplomatic tribe. They had expected to see me completely frenchified and are astounded that I can make myself understood in English and that I can hold the fork in my left hand. This connection has been very useful to me for the sale of my books.

The statistics (of Mexico) have turned the heads of our diplomats; Mr. Hammond says, they are worth a thousand pounds. He talks as if he preferred these barren tables to anything that science and imagination can produce. Well, they shall have the statistics . . . It is all written in Spanish but I am translating the manuscripts, I make comparisons with Europe according to Playfair, and I rearrange the manuscript as I want it printed to make an effective picture. I shall add (1) a large map of Mexico which is the most complete piece of work I possess, f.i. with the names of 900 mines, the new division of the provinces; (2) the large map of the valley of Mexico City, the surroundings; Robertson's is completely wrong; (3) the profile from the town of Mexico to the sea; (4) the cross-section from one ocean to the other; (5) a note on the data from which the map has been drawn . . . I hope that every English soul will feel gayer at the sight of so many piastres and even more so if they take the piastres for their fat pound sterling if we do not want to *translate* them.

With all the data I possess about the mines, the enormous exportation of silver, the trade, with the material furnished by the map and the profile, I believe that it will be a piquant work. I believe it even more when I see the effect which the *Present State of Peru* had in London according to Lord Harrowby, a translation from the Spanish *Mercurio Peruano,* distorted by a thousand ineptitudes, due to ignorance of the language and the sciences. [4]

The defeat of Prussia at the battle of Jena towards the end of 1806 and the abject surrender to Napoleon led to a complete and abrupt change in the life of the capital. The court went to East Prussia, and Berlin came under the administration of French troops. The reparations which had to be paid caused an enormous rise in prices, and food became scarce. The spirit of the country was broken. Although there had been fears before that the organization of Frederick the Great's army had become antiquated, public opinion was unprepared for the complete collapse. Humboldt withdrew into his work and escaped into his memories of the timeless world of South America. In the *Aspects of Nature* he tried to give a series of pictures of the strange scenery he had seen, the Llanoes and the forests of the Orinoco, the hunt for electric eels and a spectacular fall of meteorites. The appeal to the emotions is combined here with scientific observations, a new method of approach in which he attempted to win the attention of educated but unscientific readers for the fascination of the discovery of scientific truths. This, the first of his South American publications, was written in German and later translated into the main European languages; it ran into several editions.

His thoughts went to a return to Paris as soon as circumstances would allow it. Thus he writes to François Gérard: 'Since my return from Italy and in particular since the departure of my intimate friend GayLussac, I have lived in a moral desert. The events which have crushed our political independence like those which have led up to them and which were a pointer to the future, everything combines to make me regret my forests of the Orinoco and the solitude of a nature

75

at once majestic and benevolent. After having enjoyed great good fortune for nearly twelve years, after having wandered in distant countries, I have returned to share the misfortunes of my own country. The hope to reduce the distance between us gives me some comfort. I shall carry out this plan as soon as delicacy and my duties permit. I feel it more every day that I do good work only there where others around me do even better.'[5]

During this period of waiting, he continued his measurements of the geomagnetic field. His interest was now mainly directed towards the regular and irregular variations of the position of the compass. George Graham had discovered in 1722 that the magnetic declination, the deviation of the compass from the true north, varied in the course of the day, and Celsius in Sweden, following up these observations, found a violent perturbation of the declination at a time at which a beautiful display of the aurora borealis was visible in Upsala; Cavendish and Gilpin had shown in 1806 that the dip, the deviation from the horizontal position, also varied. The effects are very small; it is necessary to measure changes in the angle of one minute of arc, and complete freedom from outside perturbations and from mechanical shocks is needed, if reliable results are to be obtained. Humboldt had rented a small cottage in the garden of a rich brandy distiller on the outskirts of Berlin where he set up his instruments. Mr. George, the owner of the grounds, harboured an historian and a philosopher as well in his park and was inordinately proud of his learned men whose dwellings he showed off to every visitor instead of the more usual rock garden. Here, Humboldt carried out more than six thousand observations from May 1806 until June 1807. Glued to his post, he spent at one time seven days and nights in succession at his instruments taking half-hourly readings. Later, he had the help of J. Oltmanns, the young astronomer, with whom he alternated so that both could get a little sleep and still keep up the continuity of their observations. In this way, they discovered that the gradual deviation towards the east during the day was followed by a further change to the east and then a return to the west during the night, deviations which did not exceed three minutes of arc. In December, he was lucky enough to observe a display of the aurora and simultaneously a violent perturbation of the magnetic needle. These irregular pulses, periods of rest, followed by extremely fast fluctuations were soon seen to appear when no northern lights were visible. They were usually announced by smaller irregularities which occurred a few hours before the onset, and Humboldt used to invite friends for the unusual effect which he called a 'magnetic storm', a tech-nical term which later passed into international usage. The not infrequent occurrence of these violent disturbances led Hum-boldt at that time already to the idea of organizing similar research with the same kind of apparatus in places to the east and west of Berlin, but his departure for Paris and the long-continued political unrest in western Europe prevented the realization of this plan.

Seven

PARIS AND ARAGO

THIS secluded life came to an end in 1807; Humboldt was invited by the king to accompany Prince Wilhelm as his equerry on a political mission to Paris; this was the beginning of Humboldt's long stay in France. While the prince tried in direct negotiations with Napoleon to reduce the French demands for Prussian reparations, his chamberlain threw himself wholeheartedly into his scientific work. When Prince Wilhelm was forced to return with empty hands in the autumn of 1808, Humboldt asked for and was granted leave to remain in Paris to carry through the publication of his great work on the results of his American expedition, an undertaking which would have been impossible in Berlin at that time. A number of collaborators were called in to help in the evaluation of the numerical results and in the sorting and classification of the collections. Artists, Redouté and Gérard among them, and engravers were employed to produce illustrations of the scenery after Humboldt's sketches, of the plants and animals and the necessary maps, at enormous cost which was not entirely matched by the results. The technique of the romantic age led to a curiously diminishing representation of the grandiose.

In the middle of these literary activities, Humboldt neglected neither his experimental work nor his social life. His friendship with Gay-Lussac was continued. He divided his days between the École Polytechnique and the Tuileries; the nights and mornings he spent at the École where he shared a room with Gay-Lussac, his 'best friend'. Their laboratory in the basement was so damp that Gay-Lussac worked in wooden clogs; Humboldt stuck to the footwear he had worn in the American forests, high boots with turned-over tops. After only three or four hours of sleep, he got up at six o'clock and carried on with his experiments in the morning; the rest of the day until dinner he spent over the books he was writing and with the publishers and engravers. He was a very sociable man and loved conversation; even more he loved talking and usually passed his evenings wandering from one salon to the other until well after midnight, helping to spread the gossip of the town. Once he had been particularly active in discussing the guests who had just left. One young lady who had seemed to be on the point of departure, sat down again with such obvious impatience that their hostess asked if anything was wrong. 'I don't want to leave before this gentleman,' she said, 'I don't want to be discussed by him.' Humboldt was not allowed to forget this occurrence for some time.

Returned from his excursions into society, he settled down to more work and to his interminable letters, between one and two thousand every year. As a result of his hardships on the Orinoco, his right arm was permanently crippled with rheumatism which his doctors thought to be of scorbutic origin. When he wanted to write or shake hands, he had to lift up his right arm with his left hand. However, he refused to dictate his correspondence since he was afraid of losing the personal note. His atrocious scribble could only be deciphered by experts, usually some patient female relative. To make things more difficult, he had the habit of covering the margins with afterthoughts. Arago said that, to read the letters, he had to rub out the decoded bits as he went along. Considering his means and his position, he lived on an extremely modest scale. In the first few years he was in acute financial straits; some of his money, invested in Poland, had been seized as enemy property but was eventually freed. Later on, he kept a manservant and his own carriage, but his usual abode, a small set of rooms on the quais, not far from the *Institut* where he assiduously attended all the meetings, resembled ordinary students' lodgings more than the apartments of the chamberlain of the Prussian king. His study was the simplest place imaginable: very few books, some wooden chairs with cane bottoms, and, most important to him, a large deal table whose surface served as a blackboard. When the wood was covered with calculations, a carpenter came and planed it off again. In spite of his mature years and his growing reputation, he sometimes indulged in the humour of a first year undergraduate. 'I still live between sulphur and potash,' he writes to Pictet in 1808, 'between Thénard and Gay-Lussac. Ammonia, M. Berthollet, comes to see us sometimes; we all feel hydrogenated.'[1]

He was becoming very well-known, so well-known that the newspapers began to follow his comings and goings or to invent plans for him. He was kept busy contradicting scurrilous rumours such as: 'It is reported from Frankfurt that M. A. de Humboldt, the well-known traveller, intends to leave Prussia and settle in Bavaria. He has bought a monastery twelve miles from Munich.' A report that he was going to Weimar to meet Mme de Stael and Friedrich Schlegel was rather more serious for him at that time. Both of them were decided enemies of Napoleon, and Humboldt saw to a speedy denial in the *Journal de l'Empire*: 'The report of a journey of M. de Humboldt to Weimar is completely unfounded. The learned traveller continues his stay in Paris and has just published an account of 291 new observations of longitudes and latitudes, an immense labour which puts the geography of America on a new basis. It is difficult to understand how German journalists can so lightly join the name of M. de Humboldt, foreign associate of the first class of the *Institut*, with that of M. Schlegel, known for his disparagement of French literature.'

Wilhelm Humboldt had returned to Berlin in 1808 as chief of the department of education in the Ministry of the Interior, where in the following year he founded the university which now bears the name of the two brothers. When, in 1810, he was sent to Vienna as Prussian envoy, Alexander was offered his post in Berlin. He declined, however, although his situation in Paris as citizen of an enemy country, now under French occupation and with a 'resistance' movement under way, was not always easy. It became more difficult with the start of the Wars of Liberation in 1813. After the breakdown of the armistice with Napoleon, he wrote to his sister-in-law: 'My dear sister, your two letters of the 1st and 21st July have been very pleasant for me in these oppressive, sad and expectant times. Do continue to write to me through business connec- tions, dear Li, for although in these last weeks people here have had unpleasantness through careless letters from relations, I have nothing to fear of that kind from your correspondence. We touch only on family affairs and on things close to our hearts and are silent about the pressure of world-shaking events.'[2]

Only a year later, the situation was reversed: the Allied armies had entered Paris, and it was now Humboldt who, by his influence with the Prussian authorities, was able to save French scientific establishments, in particular the natural his- tory museum, 'from the blind resentment of foreign troops'. And Gérard, who had a reputation as a fashionable portrait painter, was given an opportunity to portray the victors. The Duke of Wellington, the Czar, the Prussian king and princes all sat to him in turn.

Humboldt was still a close friend of Gay-Lussac, but this relationship had been eclipsed by his affection for François Arago, which began in 1809 and ended with Arago's death in 1853, an affection which, without any sexual overtones, can only be described as the great passion of Humboldt's life. Arago, a French Catalan, was born in 1783 in a small town near Perpignan, the son of a lawyer and owner of some local vineyards. The sight of the French army in the revolutionary wars decided him to become an artillery officer. But that meant a good knowledge of mathematics if he wanted to enter the École Polytechnique, and the grammar school in Perpignan did not provide any advanced scientific training. A textbook on the calculus, discovered in a bookshop, gave Arago the opportunity to educate himself. In trepidation, the sixteen-year-old boy went to Toulouse to submit to the entrance examination at the hands of the stern and rather arbitrary Lagrange. After a tussle about his nationality—his Spanish surname made the examiner suspicious—he passed victoriously, to become in fairly early years the director of the observatory and permanent secretary of the *Institut*. His appointment in 1806 to assist Biot in the extension of the triangulation of France to Spain and the Balearic Isles led to an unexpectedly heroic incident in his scientific career. When the war between France and Spain broke out, Arago was arrested and imprisoned for nearly two years in a Spanish fort. His only idea was to save his notes and measurements for posterity and France; he had hidden his papers under his shirt, and wearing them next to his skin he starved in his Spanish dungeon, was transferred to Algiers, spent another year in an internment camp, and sailed finally to Marseilles where he arrived in the summer of 1809. While he was still in quarantine, he was at last able to hand over the results of his work, truly the worse for wear, to the authorities, and the news of his tenacity prompted Humboldt to send him a letter of congratulation to the hospital, the first letter to reach him in France. Arrived in Paris, Arago hastened to express his thanks; and that was the beginning of a remarkable friendship.

The two men had a great deal in common, in particular their liberal political opinions, and a strong spirit of independence. Intellectually, the much older Humboldt unhesitatingly acknowledged the superiority of his friend; his need for Arago's affection seems to have been greater than Arago's need for his. Arago's principles came before his personal relations. When the Prussian king came to Paris in 1814 after the downfall of Napoleon, he expressed through Humboldt his wish to visit the observatory under Arago's guidance. Arago replied that he was flattered but had no desire to see the king who had invaded France. It was Humboldt's unpleasant task to wrap this uncompromising reply in suitable language. He even tried several times to make his friend change his attitude but with-out success. One evening, Humboldt, who intended to go the next day on a short visit to London, came to say good-bye. The next morning he turned up at the observatory to take his final leave in the company of another man in travelling clothes. He was, he said, on the point of departure with the gentleman who would like to pay a short visit to the observatory; their carriage was waiting at the door. Arago showed them round willingly, and when the conversation turned to politics, he expressed his indignation at the way in which the sovereigns of the victorious countries exacted payment from France for the ambitious follies of Napoleon. Humboldt, very restless, took Arago aside and said: 'Moderate your tone; you are speaking to the king,' un-prepared for Arago's gleeful reply: 'I thought so; that's why I have been so frank.' Afterwards, Humboldt had to admit that the king had not been at all offended; in fact, he quite approved of the patriotic sentiments of the Frenchman.

The never-ending work on the South-American publica-tions went on together with experiments at the observatory, now with Arago and Gay-Lussac; as a relaxation, he drew and painted in Gérard's studio. Three times in these years after the end of the Napoleonic wars, Humboldt had to accompany his king to political negotiations, to London in 1814, to the congress of Aix-la-Chapelle in 1818, and to Verona and Rome in 1822. His journey through the Alps did not pass without a little geological study.

I have made some beautiful collections in the Euganean mountains which rise like a volcanic archipelago in the middle of the ancient sea of Lombardy. From Abano I entered the valley of Fiemme via Bassano and the lower valley of Trento. This valley is a continuation of the one become recently famous through the observations of Count Marzari Pen-cati who has seen granite above shell-bearing limestone which granulated

83

in the granitic volcanic eruption. You see, this is a great blow against the legitimacy of granite. We live in a century where nothing stays in its place. Mont Blanc together with Chimborazo have been robbed of their ancient grandeur, their very foundations have been undermined. One begins to assess the granite of the Swiss Alps and the Tyrol as of fairly recent date. To keep to my plan to be back in Verona on the 3rd of October, I drove on a dark night to Cavallese and Predazzo and followed the route of Trento and Roveredo to Verona. Quite close to it, at Ala, I was seen (would you believe it) by Leopold von Buch who has been wandering for five months in the Tyrolean mountains, on foot and without a guide, armed with an umbrella, an overcoat and a whole library in his pockets. He was not sure enough of having recognised me to stop my carriage but followed me to Verona where I spent five days with him in the most interesting mineralogical discussions. I showed him a part of my treatise on geognosy which is printed but not yet published, and he was very pleased with it to my great satisfaction. I went with him on an excursion on foot in the environs of Verona, in the basaltic valleys of San Giovanni and Ronca. Buch, without doubt the finest geologist of this century, remains a most remarkable psychological phenomenon. It is impossible to combine more eccentricity with a greater intellect and a finer character. The voluntary isolation in which he has always lived has increased his taste for independence and his irritability to the point where the mere idea of taking a guide makes him furious. I walk patiently with him for hours; he reads the map; we do not find the hamlet where we mean to spend the night; it pours with rain; we see a man in the vineyards; I should be the most detestable man in his eyes if I dared to ask the way, reassure myself about the route we have taken. Fifty years old, he marches fourteen hours daily; what he finds tiring, he says, is to have to talk constantly. Quite alone, he talks at the top of his voice. He argues with his antagonists in mineralogy (he has the mania to believe that he is generally misunderstood), he argues quite alone and finds that exhausting. From time to time, he stands still, rubs his hands with increasing rapidity, lifts them up to the sky, and with his mouth half open, pince-nez on the nose, the head thrown back, he enjoys the sunshine of Italy. He has one fixed idea to which he returns incessantly. However, side by side with granite and eupholite, he loves to repeat everything his brother tells him of the adventures of the ladies at the court of the late queen; he is aristocrat and *ultra par excellence*, and the little red ribbon to which his imagination turns amidst his enjoyment of nature, causes him a pleasure, which is not entirely philosophic. [3]

The progress of the great work on South America was as slow as it was costly. The money for the illustrations and the collaborators had to be found, partly out of Humboldt's own pockets; later he obtained a grant of £960 from the Prussian Minister of Finance. The dreams he had had of recouping the expense for the expedition out of his publications, faded gradually; he even forwent his royalties of over £1,900 to speed up the printing. The edition consisted finally of twenty volumes in folio and ten in quarto. The printing and engraving cost £24,000 and the paper £4,800. It sold unbound at £383 and bound at £412 the set. The expense was twice as great as that of the lavishly produced *Description de l'Egypte* which had been paid for by Napoleon. Very few institutions could afford to buy the complete edition; even Humboldt did not possess one. In acknowledgement of the Prussian grant, four *de luxe* copies were sent to the universities of Berlin, Breslau (Wroclaw), Halle and Bonn. The French, Russian and Austrian governments took a certain number of copies for universities and scientific institutions. After a stay of twenty years in Paris, Humboldt's private fortune was so seriously depleted that the emoluments from his position as a Prussian chamberlain were his main means of subsistence. For a further stay in France, he needed an extension of his leave of absence from the court. But a personal application to the king in 1826 was without success; he had to return to Berlin with a salary of £750 and the concession that he might spend four months in the year in Paris. In 1827, he left his beloved Paris, and after a short visit to London, accompanying there the newly appointed Prussian envoy Count Bülow, the son-in-law of his brother, he returned to Berlin where he lived until the end of his long life.

He found it hard to leave the animated intellectual life: Arago and the observatory, the bickering in the *Institut*,

Gérard's salon where painters, writers, scientists and their admirers met on Wednesdays to play cards, to make music and to talk. It was the only gathering of this kind which functioned all the year round; even in the summer when the Gérards, in common with other Parisians of means, went to live in the country, the whole family travelled to town on Wednesdays and opened the house for the one sacred evening. He became to a certain extent cut-off from the younger generation of scientists for whom he had always found time and financial support: men like Agassiz, Liebig, Boussingault owed the beginning of success to Humboldt. Boussingault, a young geologist who was going out to South America, became Humboldt's particular favourite and pupil.

Humboldt wanted first of all to get to know me, to weigh me up. He talked a great deal and very well. I listened to him as a pupil listens to a master; he was pleased that I understood the great art of listening. He showed me very soon that sincere friendship which he preserved for me until his death. He gave me several instruments which he had used in America: a pocket barometer, an artificial horizon, a prismatic compass, a celestial hemisphere by Flamsteed, precious relics of which I made the greatest use and which I left to my companion, the unfortunate colonel Hall.

He did even more; he absolutely insisted on teaching me the use of his instruments; we fixed a day to meet for this purpose. He lived at that time on the Quai Napoléon, in rooms on the fourth floor with a view of the Seine, approximately opposite the mint.

Humboldt was then fifty-five years old, with a well set-up figure of medium height, white hair, an indefinable look in his eyes, a mobile face, witty, with a few pockmarks which he had acquired in Cartagena. His dress had remained the same since the time of the *directoire*: blue coat, yellow buttons, yellow waistcoat, short trousers of striped cloth, high boots, turned over at the tops, the last existing pair in Paris in 1821, white cravat, a weary and battered hat. He dined at the Frères Proven-çaux; in the morning, he always spent an hour or two at the Café de Foy where he went to sleep after his lunch.

Our exercises with the sextant began immediately after my arrival; we measured the angle between the spire of the Invalides and the lightning conductor on the church of St. Sulpice; we also took an altitude of the sun. He left nothing out of my instructions, the means of verification, the determination of the error of collimation, all the calculations were made on the wood of the famous table. I became soon familiar with the use of the sextant and the artificial horizon.

That was Humboldt before my departure, that was how I found him after my return from America. He was then occupied with his interminable book.

Humboldt was indefatigable. In order to help me, he produced a book of instructions which has been most useful to me. He insisted that I should take with me a small collection of trachytic rocks from Hungary. He went to Beudant, the curator of the collection of Count Bournon, removed some specimens, went to a joiner, had a box made on the spot to pack them in and at ten o'clock next morning he handed the collection over to me.

We gave a farewell dinner for several scientists. It was interesting. We noticed that Humboldt did not wear his boots. He was in silk stockings and had a new hat.[4]

Humboldt's short stay in London in the spring of 1827 brought him, as usual, in contact with the most diverse circles, visits to Parliament, dinner with the Lord Chancellor and the Foreign Secretary and at Holland House. The mornings he spent at Greenwich and Kew and in ruinous bouts of shopping: 'I am a nitwit, I buy everything I see.' The frantic rush in London left him completely breathless. The highlight of his activities was a visit to the Thames tunnel at Rotherhithe which was then under construction, and where he had the unique experience of a descent to the river bed in a diving bell.

The tunnel is going well although glass, potsherds and pebbles descend into the tunnel from the bottom of the river. However, practically no water penetrates with these objects because the hole is sealed up with mud and sand whenever a stone makes an opening through fifteen feet of sand. I went down at high tide with the young Brunel in the diving bell to a depth of thirty-six feet. Stones are cemented to the bottom of the Thames there, where excavations are going on, and to make quite sure that there is no mistake, an iron rod is pushed through from below on whose end the bell is placed. Going down, I felt a damnable earache. The air penetrates the Eustachian tubes and I could feel it open paths between ear, mouth and nose. The experts tell us to counteract it with the breath and chase the air out of the ears but I was not taught to do it when I was young. The compressed air from the pump above makes it worse because the pressure is uneven. After a few minutes, I became used to it. We stayed forty minutes at the bottom. On the ascent from 56″ pressure to 28″ at the surface, small blood vessels broke in my nose and chest as on the Chimborazo; I coughed blood and had a nose bleed until the next day, but in a harmless manner. Young Brunel never bleeds; it is a Prussian privilege. The diving bell has preoccupied me more than anything I have done since I left Paris; it is very, very curious. Since the river is very dirty, you cannot see more than thirty-five feet; a lantern was lit and on going up, we found it amusing to see the water boil on our boots. We went down in jackets, and the young man and I looked like Eskimoes. Would you believe it: three months ago, two workmen were drowned in an English port because, signalling with a hammer, they managed to smash the bell which had a casting fault. On the bell, in which I went down, the chain to the crane broke about a month ago, fortunately when the bell was still above the surface, on the boat. I asked young Brunel what would happen to us when that should happen thirty-five feet below. He showed me a reserve chain leading from the rim of the bell to the boat. In this case, the bell would be turned upside down under the water and we should be pushed to the surface by the impact of the water. I found that very reassuring. As a matter of fact, accidents are exceedingly rare and when you see the assurance of the crew (ten to twelve men), you cannot feel afraid.[5]

Not quite three weeks later, the river broke into the excavations at high water, the first of these disasters which finally stopped the work on the tunnel for a long time.

IV. Pyramid of Cholula (Mexico), from 'Sites in the Cordilleras', after a sketch by Alexander von Humboldt

Eight

THE AMERICAN PUBLICATIONS

THE publication of the results of the American expedition, which had taken over twenty years, falls roughly into three parts: the scientific results and data, the treatises on the geography and economics of Cuba and Mexico, and the narrative account of the travels. The first of these were in the main published in collaboration with experts in the field. The last two, however, are completely from Humboldt's hand. With a few exceptions, they are written in French; William Hooker published, at his own expense, the collection of cryptogams in Latin; C. S. Kunth, a nephew of Humboldt's former tutor, printed the classification of the new species of plants, brought from South America, in Latin, and Humboldt wrote a German essay on the geography of plants which he dedicated to Goethe. The printing lasted from 1805 to 1836. The astronomical and geographical data were calculated from Humboldt's measurements by Oltmanns, the young astronomer who had assisted Humboldt in his magnetic observations in Berlin; Cuvier, Latreille and Valenciennes collaborated in the account of zoology and comparative anatomy. The botanical work had originally been allotted to Bonpland but he was so dilatory that in the end only two out of the six botanical publications were written by him, the others by Kunth. Even those two were not too favourably received; Robert Brown, the botanist, had the greatest doubts of the validity of his classifications.

Shortly after his return from South America, Bonpland had been appointed superintendent of the gardens of the empress Josephine at Malmaison and Navarra. In addition, he had been granted a pension of £120 as the result of a petition by Humboldt who had presented the botanical gardens in Paris with his own herbarium of American plants. Active work in the imperial gardens was more to Bonpland's liking; he cultivated rare plants and reorganized Malmaison with great success. He also became very attached to Josephine; after her early death in 1814, he lost interest in his occupation, and in 1816 he accepted a post as professor of natural history in Buenos Aires, now the capital of the newly founded republic of the Argentine. His subsequent fate was quite extraordinary. Four years after his arrival, he set out on an expedition; he intended to cross the Gran Chaco and Bolivia and explore the southern parts of the Andes. But at the very beginning of his journey he had to pass a part of the country over which there was a boundary dispute between the Argentine and Paraguay. Paraguay was at that time under the régime of the dictator Dr. Francia, a violent and suspicious man. Although Bonpland had been cautious enough to apply to him for permission to study the maté plant, he and his servants were attacked one night by a detachment of cavalry; all the servants were killed, Bonpland himself, hit over the head with a sword, was put in chains and taken into the interior of the country. For nine years he lived near Santa Maria; his movements were restricted to a small district. Later on, he was allowed to act as a surgeon to the troops garrisoned there— he had had a medical training—and even superintended the construction of roads and public buildings. Humboldt tried very hard to obtain Bonpland's release: he wrote to Francia himself and obtained support from Canning and Chateaubriand. The French scientists with Cuvier at the head went into action but without any success. In 1830, Bonpland was suddenly allowed to go, and he settled in a small town in Uruguay, not far from the Brazilian frontier. There he continued his scientific activity, organized a national museum and was given a ranch in the pampas in official recognition of his achievements. Surrounded by the children he had had by an Indian woman, he passed there the last years of his life in the most primitive circumstances. He had even given up the use of knife and fork. Until his death in 1858—he was murdered by a gaucho—he did not stop making vague plans for a return to Paris. He longed for an intellectual and civilized life, but was frightened to leave his plantations of oranges, peaches, figs and roses which he had created in the grassy plains, for the confined space of a room in town with a geranium pot on the window-sill. Although his friendship with Humboldt had never ceased, he felt a certain jealousy towards the companion whose life had taken so divergent a path.

Humboldt's own contribution to the publication of the scientific data was restricted to a volume on the geology and climatology of South America which included the geography of plants, a subject which was in the main his own creation. An astounding number of new ideas was combined with new forms of representation which have become the very basis of present-day methods. To give an idea of the real elevation of a mountain range, he introduced the distinction between the height of peaks, ridges and passes, where the ridge height is the average elevation of all the passes in a given range. It is the ridge height which determines the character and geographical importance of a range: as an example he discusses the Alps and the Pyrenees. The Alps, although they possess the highest peaks in Europe, have a comparatively low ridge and passes. Consequently, they have never been a barrier to communication between peoples; traffic has passed over them since classical times and before. The Pyrenees, however, have lower peaks but a relatively high ridge and inaccessible passes and have much more effectively separated the Peninsula from the rest of Europe. The elevations of the Andes are treated in this manner to give an easily grasped picture of the structure of the range. Another concept introduced by him is that of the vertical profile of a country; his book contains a number of drawings of vertical cross-sections of various parts of South America which show at a glance the relative extension of high-lying and low-lying districts.

When Humboldt set out on his expedition, he was a confirmed adherent of Werner's neptunism, the theory that all rocks had formed from liquid deposits. He had then already made some contributions to the ideas of his time. One of the difficulties of Werner's hypothesis was to account for the maintenance of the high temperatures needed to keep the igneous rocks in solution. Humboldt had tried in 1799 to ascribe the effect to the rise in temperature of the solution when large masses were precipitated: a large mass of rock is precipitated, the temperature of the solution rises and leads to evaporation of some of the liquid. The saturation increases and further masses are precipitated. Rapid precipitation results in amorphous deposits; a slow process is the origin of crystalline minerals. The high temperature at this stage of geological evolution is also made responsible for the tropical climate which had to be deduced from the incidence of tropical fossilized flora and fauna in northern latitudes.

At about the same time, his travels through Bavaria, Switzerland and northern Italy had convinced him that the limestone found in the Swiss Jura did not belong to the Trias period of rocks, as Werner had believed, but to a later formation which he called tentatively 'Jurassic', a term which was soon universally adopted.

His own observations of the volcanoes of the Andes produced a radical change in his opinions of the origin of volcanic rocks. He now became a volcanist; he saw the difference between eruptive and sedimentary rocks and the metamorphosis which can alter the structure of minerals in the vicinity of a volcanic explosion. The alignment of volcanoes observed in the Andes and continued into Mexico led him to the idea that mountain ranges had arisen along subterranean clefts or faults; longitudinal ranges indicate the presence of a single or several parallel faults; groups of mountains have been lifted up above an irregular network of faults. 'Are alpine ranges arisen on clefts just like the volcanic peaks in the plain of Jorullo?' This violence in natural processes struck a good many people as very undesirable in the light of the political events of the time. Characteristic was Goethe's attitude who refused to acknow/ ledge the validity of Plutonism; he vastly preferred a slow and orderly evolution to this revolutionary upheaval.

Humboldt had also some very pertinent things to say about the propagation of seismic waves, be it underground or on the surface. He pointed out that they can travel along or across faults and that the underground wave may pass below districts where no surface effect is felt.

The studies of climatology and the geography of plants were very dear to Humboldt. His stay in a tropical climate gave him the ideal opportunity to obtain through a systematic series of observations over a number of years an insight into the periodic changes of temperature and barometric pressure at different heights above sea level. In Europe, local perturbations of the weather are so strong that general laws can only be discerned after collecting mean values over a very long time. In a tropical climate, however, the variations are so regular that primary and secondary phenomena are much sooner disentangled. Hum/ boldt's attention was in the main directed towards the inter/ pretation of large/scale phenomena: the origin of the trade winds, the influence of warm or cold sea currents on the climate of adjacent coastal districts, the distribution of average yearly temperatures as a function of geographical latitude and height above sea level, and the effects of the climatological factors on the occurrence of different plant and animal species. He was intent on discovering general laws but aware that the collection of accurate data over a sufficiently long period was the first prerequisite for any subsequent theorising; again and again he stresses the importance of conscientiously acquired mean values. 'Before discovering the laws of nature, it is necessary to examine the causes of local perturbations and to obtain a knowledge of the average state of the atmosphere and the recur/ rent type of its variations. Of the whole picture presented to us by physics, only the facts are stable and certain. The theories, children of our opinions, are variable like them. They are the meteors of the intellectual world, seldom beneficent and more often harmful for the intellectual progress of mankind.'[1]

Humboldt's tables of the temperature of the surface of the Atlantic Ocean which he had measured on his crossing from Spain to Cumana, drew the remark from the *Quarterly Review*: 'We could never discover any hope of advantage to the interests of navigation from observations on the temperature of the ocean.'[2] However, the determination of the low temperatures of the current along the Peruvian coast has been immortalized in the name 'Humboldt current'.

The detailed observations of the various meteorological data in Central and South America were published in the form of tables; for every locality, the average summer and winter temperatures are given. For the purpose of giving an immediate picture of these figures, Humboldt adopted a method introduced in 1701 by Halley in his map of the magnetic declination over the earth's surface, the graphical representation. On a map, he connected the points of equal mean annual temperature by curves for which he coined the well-known term 'isothermal lines'. They are seen to deviate from the circles of geographical latitude, deviations which depend on the height above sea level, the distance from the coast, the proximity of warm or cold sea currents, etc. Humboldt's equatorial projection was replaced by Brewster by a polar projection when the new polar stations had provided sufficient data. This form of representation was extended by Humboldt to the lines of equal magnetic intensity, the isodynamics, and of equal magnetic dip, the isoclines, all terms of his invention.

The geography of plants, the knowledge of the climatic conditions under which different vegetations are to be found, is most strikingly demonstrated in the tropics wherever high mountains rise near the equator; the vegetation changes from the tropical flora in the plain to that of high northern latitudes on the peak. All the climates of the world are there contained within a few miles of vertical elevation. The first rudiments of this subject were recognized by Reinhold Forster on his journey with Cook, and by the French scientists Ramond and Soulavié in the highlying regions of southern France. To Humboldt we owe the systematic tabulation of plant life in connection with meteorological and geographical data. 'I have drawn several profiles and geographical maps with hygrometric, electrometric, eudiometric, etc., levels to determine the physical qualities which have so much influence on vegetable physiology so that I can indicate in feet the height at which every tree is found in the tropics.'[3] In this respect, it is important to separate the mean summer and winter temperatures from the annual average. 'If we begin in the thermal scale of cultivated plants with those which demand the hottest climate, i.e. with vanilla, cocoa, pisang, and cocopalms and descend to pineapple, sugar cane, fruitbearing date trees, cotton, lemon trees, olives, chestnuts and drinkable wine, we are taught by an accurate discussion of the geographical limits of cultivation in the plain and on the slope of mountains that here climatic conditions other than the mean yearly temperature become operative. To mention only the culture of the vine, I recall that the production of drinkable wine demands an annual temperature of more than 49°; not only that, but a mild winter of more than 33° must be followed by an average summer temperature of at least 64°. At Bordeaux, in the valley of the Garonne (latitude 44° 50'), the temperatures are: for the year 57°, for the summer 71°, for the autumn 58° and for the winter 43°. In the Baltic plains (latitude $52\frac{1}{2}°$) where indigestible wines are produced and even drunk, the figures are: 47°, 64°, 47° and 30°. It may appear strange that the difference between climates favouring or inhibiting the cultivation of vines are not more strongly indicated by the thermometer; it is not quite so strange when we consider that a thermometer, placed in the shade and protected from direct insolation and nocturnal radiation, does not in all seasons of the year measure the true surface temperature of the soil which receives all the solar radiation.'[4]

Humboldt published an account of his travels for the non-scientific, educated public which was planned to cover the whole five years of the expedition; only the period from 1799 to 1801 was, however, described in the end, from the departure from Spain to the return from the Orinoco basin. The original three volumes of the French edition had expanded to seven in the English translation which was published under the title *Personal Narrative of Travels to the Equinoctial Regions of the New Continent during the years 1799–1801*. It had been his intention to combine a report of his impressions of tropical nature and the conditions of the country with reflections on his scientific activities. In all his writings, he was given to prolixity; completely unable to keep to an orderly sequence of events and ideas, he produced a miscellany of descriptions, figures, reflections and history, sometimes fascinating, sometimes wearying. He was well aware of his faults: 'To dare to give titles to the chapters, one must bring order into one's ideas and suppress what is extraneous to the principal point. And that is what I cannot do.'[5] The work is still, however, a source of information about the Venezuela of that time. In England, it was not very well received:

As we always felt, so we have no hesitation to declare, a sincere respect for the talent and various qualifications of M. de Humboldt; at the same time it would be uncandid to conceal our opinion, that, both as a philosopher and a writer, he has his faults; the most prominent of which perhaps are, a too great fondness, in the one, for generalization, or for grouping a small number of facts into systems; and in the other, for mixing up the details and minutiae of scientific observations with the general narrative.

Having thus narrowed our objections to two points, we cheerfully offer the praise to which he is justly entitled for ardent zeal, determined perseverance, and unwearied research; to these we may add, a warmth of feeling and a force of imagination, which, if education and early habit had not controlled her purpose, and converted the possessor into a philosopher, nature evidently intended to form the poet. No writer knows better than M. de Humboldt how to seize a subject and exhibit it in the most striking points of view; and by a happy faculty of grouping, or contrasting, the meanest and most familiar objects, to give them an interest to which, separately considered, they could have no pretension. . . . His great merit, however, is that of seeing every thing, and leaving nothing unsaid of what he sees;—not a rock nor a thicket, a pool or a rivulet,—nay, not a plant nor an insect, from the lofty palm and the ferocious alligator, to the humble lichen and half-animated polypus, escapes his scrutinizing eye, and they all find a place in his book.

We shall content ourselves with observing, that he is so deeply versed in the study of nature, and possessed of such facility in bringing to bear, on every object that arrests his attention, so vast a fund of knowledge, that we may say of him, in physics, what was said of Barrow in divinity, that he never quits a subject till he has exhausted it.

But this very facility, which perhaps may be thought the highest praise that could be bestowed, as applied to a series of philosophical essays, or distinct dissertations on physical subjects, becomes a fault in the personal narrative of voyages or travels; at least the bulk of readers will be very apt to lay down the book on finding the thread of the story perpetually interrupted by a learned disquisition of a dozen pages on the geognostical constitution of a chain of mountains, or the lines of isothermal temperature.[6]

Towards the end, the reviewer relented a little:

To say merely that we have been pleased with the narrative and observations which this circumnavigation (for we may call it so) of five great rivers of America has produced, would convey but an imperfect expression of our own feelings, and of that tribute to the merits of M. de Humboldt to which he is so eminently entitled. The views he has taken of this magnificent country are so clear, so detailed, and comprehensive, that the reader has perpetually before him a panorama of the surrounding objects as he travels along. The features of the route, it is true, are of the grandest and most striking description; but where the lord of the creation plays so subordinate a part as in the forests of the Equinoctial regions of the New World, it required the talent and the research of a Humboldt to give to his observations and descriptions that degree of interest which those volumes will be found to possess. Dull and wearisome as many

parts of his discussions certainly are, we toil through them with the cer⁄
tainty that some ingenious theory, some beautiful illustration, some
curious facts will be brought to elucidate the point in question.[7]

In *Views of the Cordilleras and Monuments of the Indigenous
Nations of the New Continent*, published in 1810, a curious
mixture is offered to the public of descriptions of picturesque
sites in the mountains and of the art and civilization of the
Indian population. The author states his programme in the
'Introduction' to the 'Personal Narrative':

This work is meant to display a few of the great scenes of nature in the
lofty chain of the Andes, and at the same time throw some light on the
ancient civilization of the Americans, from the study of their monu⁄
ments of architecture, their hieroglyphs, their religious rites, and their
astrological reveries. I have given in this work descriptions of the Teo⁄
calli or Mexican pyramids, compared with that of the temple of Belus,
the arabesques which cover the ruins of Mitla, idols in basalt, ornamented
with the calantica of the heads of Isis; and a considerable number of
symbolical paintings, representing the serpent woman who is the
Mexican Eve; the deluge of Coxcox, and the first migrations of the
natives of the Aztec race. I have endeavoured to prove the analogies which
exist between the calendar of the Toltec and the catasterisms of their
zodiac, and the division of time of the people of Tartary and Tibet, as
well as the Mexican traditions of the four regenerations of the globe, the
Pralayas of the Hindu and the four ages of Hesiod. I have also included
in this work, in addition to the hieroglyphical paintings I brought back
to Europe, fragments of all the Aztec manuscripts which are found at
Rome, Veletri, Vienna and Dresden, and of which the last reminds us
by its linear symbols of the kuas of the Chinese. Together with the rude
monuments of the natives of America, the same volume contains
picturesque views of the mountainous countries which these people have
inhabited, such as those of the cataract of Tequendama, of Chimborazo,
of the volcano of Jorullo and of Cayambe, the pyramidal summit of which,
covered with perennial ice, is situate directly under the equinoxial line.

In this book, western Europe was for the first time con⁄
fronted with a discussion of Aztec art and architecture, their
hieroglyphic writing and calendar, and their mythology as

objects of serious research. With his usual thoroughness, he had searched all the sources available to him, the Italian archives for manuscripts, and the Spanish writings to which he obtained access in Mexico. He became familiar with Cortés' letters and Clavigero's *History of Mexico* on whose authority he relied more than was customary at the time. The cycles of the Mexican calendar are interpreted with the help of an engraving of the calendar stone in Mexico city. The structure of the pyramid at Cholula and the legends of the four eras which all ended in a catastrophe destroying the world, one of them a flood with but one human couple saved who found their ark had foundered on the top of a mountain when the waters subsided, induced Humboldt to speculation about analogies between the Mexican mythology and the great religions of the world. His views roused the unfriendly reviewer of the *Quarterly Review* to a very frenzy of disbelief and scorn:

We do not mean to deny that the first attempts, however rude, of an unenlightened people to register events, communicate ideas and render visible the operations of the mind, are void of interest; on the contrary, we consider them as so many landmarks by which we trace, in the most interesting manner, the progress of the intellectual faculties of man; but we wish to discountenance that perverse ingenuity which would mould and twist them to its own purposes and give them a meaning which they were never intended to bear.

Neither do we mean to deny that this people had their calendar and their chronology. The alternate procession and recession of the shadows of fixed objects, to and from their extreme points, which have attracted the attention of all agricultural and consequently stationary people, would in the course of a few years' observation, give them the four great divisions of the sun's revolution; still, we cannot admit with our author that a nation so barbarous as the Mexicans had any knowledge of the *causes* of eclipses or the Metonic period of nineteen years. A picture language or such rude representations of the objects of sense as village children chalk on walls and barndoors, are the first and rudest efforts to record ideas, and the alescores of a village landlady the first approach to symbolic writing, and with both of these even the wild Hottentots called bushmen, the very lowest perhaps of the human race, appear to be acquainted. . . . The Mexicans may have advanced but, we believe, not a great way, beyond the village children, the landladies and the bush, men. 'In them,' says Robertson, 'every figure of man, of quadrupeds, of birds, as well as every representation of inanimated nature, is extremely rude and awkward. The hardest Egyptian style, stiff and imperfect as it was, is more elegant. The *scrawls of children* delineate objects almost as accurately.' Whatever therefore may have been their condition in the *tenth* century, 'when', our author says, 'they were more advanced in civilisation than Denmark, Sweden and Russia', they were sunk low enough in the fifteenth century.[7]

This diatribe against exotic art, which reads like an opening speech of an academy member on either side of the iron curtain, is linked with grave aspersions on the authenticity of the cosmogonies; the similarities to biblical stories are supposed to have been fraudulently engendered by 'pious monks'. The conclusion of the review throws heavy-handed ridicule on Humboldt's scholarship:

We have dwelt but little, and that little will perhaps be thought too much, on those cycles and calendars, those chronologies and cosmogonies extracted out of the—to us, at least—unintelligible daubings designated under the name of the 'Codices Mexicani'. To M. de Humboldt, however, they would appear to be of first-rate importance, and some idea may be formed of his laborious 'Researches' (in the libraries of Europe) to collect and explain those Sybilline documents, and to trace in their dark and mysterious leaves, the 'parallels' and 'analogies' between the several natives of the old world and the Aztecs, the Toltecs, the Cicimecs and Tlascaltecs,—from the list which he has given, rather ostentatiously, as we think, of authors or works referred to at the end of the second volume, occupying fifteen pages, and containing the names of about two hundred and forty different authors or books of all ages, nations and languages, from the Bible to Carey's Pocket Atlas, from the Iliad to some obscure magazine.[7]

Humboldt, as so many visitors after him, was immensely attracted by the grandeur of Mexican scenery, the exotic

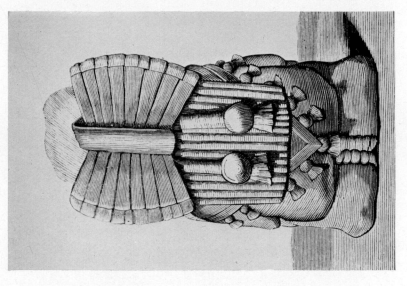

V. Statue of an Aztec priestess, from 'Sites in the Cordilleras', after sketches by Alexander von Humboldt

fascination of the old Indian civilization, and the prospects of the country. After four years in the wilderness, he had returned to a cultivated and cultured territory. His travels in the mining and agricultural districts and his prolonged stay in Mexico City with its libraries and university institutions provided him with the material for his book on the economics of Mexico, the *Political Essay on the Kingdom of New Spain*, a work which has had great influence on the investment of French and English capital in that country. He wrote a first sketch in Spanish for his hosts; the final publication, which appeared in French in 1808, was a more elaborate version. It is divided into six books starting with a discussion of the extent and physical features of Mexico and a discussion of the population and the social position of the castes. The rest of the book deals with the economy of the country and contains accounts of the population statistics, compared with those of European countries, of the produce of agriculture and the mines, of the progress of trade and manufacture and the revenues of the state. The project for building a canal between the Atlantic and the Pacific oceans occasions a discussion of the possibilities of all the sites which had been proposed for what finally became the Panama Canal. The accompanying maps used Mercator's projection, although Humboldt admitted that he would have preferred Murdoch's stereographic projection; they were based on his own determination of longitudes and latitudes and on the data provided by Spanish explorers. Following Playfair's method, he added graphical representations of statistical figures: 'It would be ridiculous to express in curves moral ideas, the well-being of a people, or the decadence of their literature. But everything concerning size and quantity, can be properly represented by geometrical figures. Statistical projections, which speak to the eye without wearying the mind, have the advantage of fixing the attention on a great number of important facts.' The spoil brought back by Humboldt and Bonpland from Mexico included, apart from a large collection of plants, axolotls, a large lump of meteoric nickel iron and seeds of the *gyrocarpus*, all new to Europe.

The main purpose of the *Political Essay* lay in drawing the attention of statesmen to the great riches and immense possibilities of this Central American country and to the economic and political means of obtaining the greatest profit from it. He justifies the connexion between geography and economics in the following words: 'The physiognomy of a country, the grouping of the mountains, the extension of plateaux, the elevation which determines the temperature, everything appertaining to the geographical configuration, has an essential relation to the progress of the population and the well-being of the inhabitants. This configuration influences the state of agriculture, varying with the climate, the possibility of internal trade, the communications, more or less favoured by the nature of the terrain, and finally the military defence on which the external safety of the colony depends. From this point of view alone, great geological surveys become of interest to the statesman as he computes the forces and the territorial riches of nations.'[8] The interest to European colonizers lies in the fact that Mexico has the characteristics of the temperate climate. Humboldt was convinced that it could, if properly cultivated, produce as much as the rest of the world produced at his time. But the greatest wealth of the country lay in the silver mines which, surrounded by forests and agricultural districts, are easily exploited. In 1803, the income from mining rights and the minting of silver coins accounted for 43 per cent of the revenue which contained such quaint items as taxes on cockfights and the sale of snow; next in importance was the indirect taxation of food with 28 per cent, and the Indian tribute, a head tax, with 10 per cent. The wealth of the mine-owners, all members of the Spanish nobility, was comparable with that of the English landowners and the East India merchants. In Mexico City, Humboldt had seen more gold and silver dishes in private houses than in France or England. Vast sums were spent on public buildings and academic institutions. The mining college alone under the direction of Del Rio, a fellow student of Humboldt at the school of mines in Freiberg, had a yearly grant of £24,000. Practical progress, however, in a more scientific exploitation of the pits and the extraction of the metal was retarded by the political rigidity of the administra-tion. The teaching in the academic institutions, which included an academy of painting and sculpture, was free, and evening classes were held for artisans of all races and social levels.

Particular attention was given to the population statistics. Since the first census had been held in 1794, Humboldt had to collect the data for 1803 from parish registers. He showed that, contrary to popular conceptions, the number of Indians was on the increase. Following the procedure of Malthus, whose work he called one of the most profoundest works on political econ-omy ever published, he prepared a list of the excess of births over deaths in those countries of which figures could be obtained, and related the rate of mortality to the climatic conditions of the district. A comparison of the number of people over fifty years proved that there was no significant difference between the different races. Only 16 per cent of the population was white, and the number of immigrants from Europe amounted to no more than 800 annually.

The position of the lower classes, and that meant the Indians, attracted his particular attention:

The history of the lower classes of a nation is the story of the events which, by creating a great inequality of fortune, of enjoyment and indi-vidual happiness, have placed one part of the people under the tutelage of the other. This story we seek almost in vain in the annals of history; they conserve the memory of great revolutions, of wars, of conquests and other scourges which have afflicted mankind. But they teach us little about the more or less deplorable fate of the poorest and most numerous class of society. Only in a very small part of Europe does the man who tills the land, freely enjoy the fruits of his labour, and this civil liberty, we must confess, is not so much the result of an advanced civilisation as the effect of those violent crises in which one class or one state has profited from the dissensions of the others. A true improvement of social institutions depends doubtless on the intellectual enlightenment and development, but the springs that set a class in motion are so intricately linked that this development can make a marked progress in one part of the nation without improving the situation of the lower classes. This saddening experience is confirmed in nearly the whole of northern Europe; there are countries there where, in spite of the vaunted civilisation of the upper classes of society, the labourer lives to-day in the same degradation as three or four centuries ago.

Mexico is the country of inequality. Nowhere perhaps exists a more frightful inequality in the distribution of wealth, of civilisation, of culti- vation of the soil, and of the population. The interior of the country possesses four towns, only one or two days' journey distant from each other, which have respectively 35,000, 67,000, 70,000 and 135,000 inhabitants. The central plateau from la Puebla de los Angelos to Mexico and beyond to Salamanca and Zelaya is covered with villages and hamlets like the most cultivated parts of Lombardy. East and west of this narrow band spreads untilled ground where there are not ten or twelve people in ten square miles. The capital of the country and other towns have academic institutions comparable with those in Europe. The architecture of public and private buildings, the elegance of the interior decorations, the carriages, the luxury of the dresses, the whole tone of society, everything has a refinement in the greatest contrast to the naked- ness, the ignorance and coarseness of the lower classes. This immense inequality of wealth is not a prerogative of the white caste (European or Creole); it is even found among the natives.

The Mexican Indians, seen in the mass, present a picture of profound misery. Relegated to the less fertile districts, indolent by nature and even more so by their political situation, they live only for the day. It is almost impossible to find among them men who enjoy a moderate fortune. In the intendancies of Oaxaca and Valladolid, in the valley of Toluca and in particular in the environs of the large town of la Puebla de los Angelos, exist some Indians who, under the appearance of poverty, conceal con- siderable riches. When I visited the little town of Cholula, an old Indian woman was just being buried who had left her children agave plantations of a value of more than £14,000. These plantations are the vineyards and the wealth of the country. However, there are no caciques in Cholula;

the Indians there are all tributary and are distinguished by their gentle and peaceful manners and by a great sobriety. The manners of Cholula are in singular contrast to those of their neighbours in Tlascala, a great number of whom pretend to be descended from the highest nobility and who increase their misery by their taste for lawsuits and by a restless and quarrelsome mind. They are looked up to by the tributary Indians; but they go normally barefoot; covered with the Mexican tunic of a coarse, brownish-black weave, they are clothed like the lowliest of the indigenous race.

The Indians are exempt from all indirect taxation; the law permits them every freedom in the sale of their produce. It is to be hoped that the court of Madrid which since early times has protected this unfortunate class, may uphold this immunity as long as they are subject to the direct taxation of the tributes. This tax is a veritable head tax which all male Indians between the age of five and fifty years have to pay. In the see of Mechoacan and in the greater part of Mexico, this tax amounts to nine shillings annually. In addition, the Indians pay to the parish eight shillings for a baptism, sixteen shillings for the marriage certificate and twenty-five shillings for a burial. To these forty-nine shillings which the church levies on every Indian, must be added twenty to twenty-four shillings for the voluntary offering, so-called. If the legislation of Queen Isabella and the Emperor Charles V appears to favour the Indians as far as taxation is concerned, it has, on the other hand, deprived them of the most important rights enjoyed by the other citizens. In a century when it was seriously debated whether Indians are reasoning beings, it was considered a good deed to treat them as minors, to put them in perpetuity under the tutelage of the whites and declare null and void any contract signed by a native of the copper-coloured race, any obligation over the value of twelve shillings entered into. These laws are rigorously enforced; they put insurmountable barriers between the Indians and the other castes whose intermixing is equally prohibited. Thousands of inhabitants cannot make a valid contract, condemned to perpetual minority, they become a burden to themselves and to the state in which they live.[8]

Humboldt, the former inspector of mines, had made a detailed investigation of Mexican mines and mining methods which were in many respects ludicrously backward. No machinery was in use; in some mines, the bags of ore were drawn up on ropes to the surface, as was the underground water, 'a truly barbarous custom'. Not unnaturally, these ropes had to be replaced nearly every week. Even worse, in other mines the ore was brought up the shafts by ladders of about 1,800 steps by the miners, needless to say, all Indians. These men carried loads of 200 to 350 pounds on their backs; they could only do this kind of work for three days of the week. The dressing of the ore was equally clumsy and the precious metal was extracted by amalgamation with mercury which made the mines greatly dependent on the mercury production of Spain and increased the price unreasonably. About 5,000 men were employed to tread the mush of mercury oxide and pounded metal with their bare feet; to Humboldt's surprise, they remained quite healthy in this occupation and showed no traces of mercury poisoning. In the early years of the conquest a great many Indians had died from the exhausting work, but in the eighteenth century, the Spaniards had started to treat this important class of workmen with more consideration. The labour in the mines was voluntary, in contrast to Peru. 'Nowhere do the people enjoy in greater security the fruit of their labours than in the mines of Mexico; no law forces the Indian to choose this species of labour or to prefer one mine to the other; and when he is displeased with the proprietor of the mine, he may offer his services to another master who may per/haps pay more regularly. These unquestionable facts are very little known in Europe.'[8] This respect for the national im/portance of the miner was even reflected in his pay: his wages were higher than those of an European miner; he obtained between 20 and 24 shillings for a working week of six days. They also got away with a good deal of stolen metal although they were searched on leaving the mines. In one mine alone, the value of looted minerals amounted to nearly £5,000 a year.

This account of the mineral riches of Mexico had a great influence on the investment of English and French capital in this country. English interests had already been awakened in the early years of the nineteenth century by reports from Peru and the *Political Essay* was immediately translated into English. The great opportunity came with the liberation of the country from Spain. During the revolution preceding the declaration of independence in 1821, many of the mines had been abandoned and filled with water, and their impoverished owners were only too thankful to sell the now useless source of their former riches. The first enterprise was started in 1822 in Paris at the instigation of the Mexican Minister of the Interior and Foreign Affairs, Alaman, who was himself an owner of gold and silver mines. The French project was to invest about £160,000 in this Franco-Mexican Company, and Humboldt was offered the position of chairman of the board of directors and European consultant with an allotment of shares to the value of £20,000. He refused the offer, just as in 1825 he declined to negotiate on behalf of the Mexican government with the cabinets of Vienna and St. Petersburg for a treaty with the new independent states of America. 'The more frankly I express my opinions in my books, the more I am disinclined to become involved in political negotiations which (however worthy their purpose might be) would in no way be seemly for my position. My disinclination for public affairs has been the reason for my repeated refusal of the honourable offers made to me by my sovereign. You know how much I have been provoked by the mere idea of lending my name to the direction of the mining company or of accepting plainly honorary titles in new scientific establishments. With this mental attitude for which I am known, with this innate horror for everything appertaining to the alleged mysteries of diplomacy, how could I be tempted to deviate from a position to which I have adhered for a long time and which seems the only one tenable for a man of letters living in a foreign country.'[9]

The Franco-Mexican Association was eventually founded under the directorship of Alaman with a capital of £240,000, which was held in 600 shares; the French venture was not very successful and was finally transferred to London, where it was reorganized under the name of United Mexican Association. The company did not exploit the mines directly but purchased the ore and dealt with the smelting and refining of silver. From now on, Mexican mining passed predominantly into English hands. The first enterprise was followed by the Anglo-Mexican Association with 10,000 shares at £100 each; it owned mines in the district of Real de Guanajuato. A third undertaking, 'The Adventurers in the Mines of Real del Monte' (sixty miles north of the city of Mexico), was founded by people who had extensive interests in English mines, whose director, the well-known mining engineer John Taylor, was put in charge of the reorganization of their property in Mexico. The Franco-Mexican Company, a joint stock company, traded in the names of the original founders Alaman, Vial and Company, with Alaman at the head. Their 6,000 shares were valued at £40 each. The figures given by Humboldt in his book had raised the most extravagant hopes for high profits in the public. By 1825, however, it had become apparent that a good deal of capital and well-directed effort were still needed to put the mines in working order; the smell of seemingly easy money had also attracted the attention of speculators who drove the share prices up before any work had started in the mines. Warning articles began to appear in the papers. *The Times* wrote on 4 July, 1825: 'A new undertaking was announced on Saturday for working the "mines of Guanajuato". Of its character and prospects it may be sufficient to say that on application to a person, calling himself the Secretary, to know the names of the directors or the trustees who were to be responsible for the appropriation of the money paid in, he refused to give any information of the subject. This difficulty did not deter many persons from making payments, and the shares were actually sold—by what manoeuvre we are unable to explain—at a high premium. We could not learn into what banking firm the deposits were to be paid. Surely some means might be devised either by the committee of the Stock Exchange or by the bankers who keep the account for undertakings of a doubt-ful character, for preventing that imposition to which the public for want of proper information are subjected. There can be no better clue to their real history than the state of the cash account. We do not affirm that the undertaking above-mentioned is actually a fraudulent one; but there is much cause of suspicion in the mode of ushering it into notice which at least calls for inquiry before giving it any support.' All the reasons for apprehension, quoted here, the lack of publicity about the qualifications of the directors and the absence of a public accounting system, led nearly twenty years later to the introduction of the Companies Act.

The need to rescue these undertakings from collapse and to reassure the public induced John Taylor to publish in 1825 his 'Statements respecting the profits of mining in Mexico. In a letter to Thomas Fowell Buxton Esq. M.P.' Sir Thomas Fowell Buxton as the principal shareholder in the Real del Monte company had the best of reasons for being concerned. Taylor starts out by giving a careful assessment of the various items of expenditure in English mines together with an estimate of the corresponding costs in Mexico. To compensate for the risks attendant on the varying output of richer and poorer veins, the capital should be spread over a great number of mines in accordance with the practice usually followed in England. He believed that, with prudent administration, 30 to 50 per cent clear profit might be secured from the Mexican venture, since there the veins of ore were more abundant than in England.

The collateral evidence to support the probabilities of such expectations is to be derived from the great amounts of profit formerly acquired, and the statements of the proportion of costs in working mines to the actual amount of value of return. Many particulars of this kind are before the public and particularly in the works of the Baron Humboldt: they have,

I know, excited the ridicule of some, and have been treated seriously by others as exaggerations brought forth to tempt the unwary. I apprehend, however, with proper deference to the wit of the one and to the caution of the others, that the fact of enormous profit in many cases rests upon very good evidence; and supposing that there were also very numerous cases of loss which is admitted, that will only prove what I am all along ready to admit, that mining to be profitable must be attended with skill and care in choosing and conducting the undertakings.

My inference from the whole is that mining is neither, as the public seemed to think a few months since, a certain source of immeasurable wealth, to be obtained by every one who was lucky enough to get a share in any mine, in any place and under any kind of management, nor is mining, as it seems now the fashion to designate it, all a bubble, cheat and delusion. . . . The proper limitation of capital will in my opinion in Mexico be to that amount of which the application can be effectively and judiciously directed. . . . In Mexico, the number of unoccupied mines is still very great but though that is the case, it is not capital alone that will work them. A great quantity of skill, experience and of labour also is required, and therefore, as the number both of able managers and experienced workmen is limited, so must be the extent of prudent enterprise.[10]

The prospects of 50 per cent clear profit proved stronger than the sensible advice to limit the extent of capitalization. The share values were driven up to absurd heights, and in the end the bubble burst. Towards 1830, the Mr. Merdles and their dupes were ruined, and Humboldt, who had acted in good faith and without any self-interest, was publicly attacked as responsible, to his great indignation. The *Quarterly Review* summed up the events of the year 1825 in the words: 'a year in which some very wise people concluded, from certain superficial appearances, that the nation was in some danger of bursting with a plethora of prosperity, and required a few waste pipes or safety valves to relieve the pressure; and these, indeed, were so abundantly supplied that the danger of repletion, being speedily removed, was followed by a no less danger from the copious evacuations of the patient which soon reduced the fulness both of his habit and his pocket. . . . There were two distinct classes of our countrymen concerned in promoting the ruinous speculations to which we have alluded—the honest and well intentioned—and the knavish and fraudulent. Of the former, some had been deceived by the exaggerated view given of the mines by the ingenious Humboldt. Others seem to have lost sight of the fact that most of the richest mines had been worked out; and that the rest through the discontinuance of working since the revolution had been filled with water or rubbish. Then some of the leading projectors were so conceited as to imagine that the Mexicans, after the experience of two centuries, knew not how to work their mines to the best advantage, or to reduce the ores. . . . The second or knavish class cared not one farthing whether the mines were productive or not. By fraud and trickery, and by putting in practice every art in which gamblers and swindlers are conversant and in which several persons in elevated ranks in society were strongly suspected of being concerned, the trafficking in shares was carried to such an extent as can only be paralleled by the once famous, or rather infamous, *tulipomania* of Holland. For instance the selling price in one mine, that of Real del Monte, was mounted up from its original price, by a series of fraudulent tricks, false reports and fictitious sales, to £1,500 for which, we suspect, the present holder would be glad to obtain about so many shillings, and whose real value may probably be not worth as many pence.'[11]

Nine

RETURN TO BERLIN

IN May 1827, Humboldt returned to Berlin and settled in a flat in the centre of the town, not far from Unter den Linden, not for very long though; the house was demolished to make room for the new museum buildings. The new abode, a first-floor flat in a by no means fashionable district, remained his home until his death. For the first time in his life, he settled down in a proper establishment, supervised by a married couple, a young and handsome ex-rifleman, Johann Seifert and his wife. His nomadic life was not over, however; his duties as a royal chamberlain compelled him to follow the court to the palaces at Potsdam and to accompany the king on his regular visits to the Bohemian spas. Regular journeys to Paris, to renew the contact with Arago, were a necessity for him. He was completely inured to the discomforts of travel; a voyage to Rome meant less to him than a visit of St. Cloud to a hardened Parisian.

He found the political situation of his country, at the time of his return, very little to his liking. After the enthusiasm for political freedom, raised by the wars against Napoleon, and the hopes for a constitution and parliamentary representation, Prussia had fallen into a state of indecision. The plans for a constitution were delayed and protracted beyond the limits of human patience. The press and public speech, obeying Metternich's dictates, were under heavy censorship. The aristocracy clamoured for restitution of their privileges; a great many writers and university people were under arrest for their subversive activities or even thoughts, people who had been heroes in the fight against Napoleon. The student organizations had been disbanded and prohibited, and all public meetings, even of scientists and scholars, were suspect. The reforms, instituted before 1813 by the chancellor Prince Hardenberg, had come to a standstill, and Hardenberg himself took the lead in prevent⁄ ing the implementation of former promises. Another 'revolu⁄ tion which never happened' had died at birth. The newly acquired rights, the liberation of the peasants, the freedom of trade from the dictatorship of the guilds and the emancipation of the Jews were in constant danger of revision. Wilhelm Humboldt had become a victim of the reactionary politics of the years after the wars; after a brilliant career as Prussian envoy in Vienna where he had taken part in the Vienna Congress, and as head of the legation in London, he had been nominated Minister for Home Affairs in 1819. He came imme⁄ diately into conflict with Hardenberg's changed outlook and was dismissed in 1820. The death of the Chancellor in 1822 produced no change in the political trends and Wilhelm never took office again. From then on, he administered his estates and continued very actively his studies of comparative philology. The intellectual life of Berlin fell into a stupor under the heavy hand of the official censor; secret informers reported private conversations, overheard in the streets and beerhouses, to the police, and school teachers were taken in charge on the accusa⁄ tion of their pupils. And yet, there was a certain laxness and inconsistency about this supervision. The authorities did not raise any objections when the Ministry of Foreign Affairs moved into a house which was owned and inhabited by a publisher and bookseller who was under police surveillance on account of his political opposition to the régime. It was left to the grumbling informers to distinguish between the sheep and the goat among the people who went in and out of the building.

The *ultras*, the members of the aristocracy and the ultra⁄ conservative elements in the professional classes, watched every step which Alexander Humboldt took when he first came to

Berlin. They were outraged at the presence of a 'revolutionary' at the court of the king. For months, the rumour went round that he was never seen inside the palace because the royal family did not wish to receive him, until it was discovered that he had simply chosen not to appear. His duties as chamberlain were adapted to his special gifts and knowledge: he had to give reports on scientific and artistic affairs and not, as usual, on political matters. The king, Frederick William III, left the actual government in the hands of the cabinet. Later, during the reign of Frederick William IV, he had to conduct negotiations with the ministers of finance and education himself in those scientific and artistic projects which he wanted to further. He was always very active in his efforts to obtain money for men and institutions; Berlin owed the construction and equipment of a new observatory to his endeavour.

For the first time since their student days, the brothers Humboldt were united again, a reunion to which Alexander, at any rate, had looked forward. Wilhelm's attitude to his brother was affectionate and critical at the same time. There were moments when Alexander got on his nerves. The inexorable flow of his conversation irritated him; Alexander's admiration for French civilization offended his patriotism. Alexander preached on the superiority of Ingres and Delacroix and Wilhelm preferred Rauch and Thorvaldsen, Germanic depth to Gallic shallow showiness, so-called. As a humanist, he considered the arts his own preserve anyway. He objected, in spite of his professedly liberal opinions, to his brother's radicalism, his preference for liberal circles in Paris and the Whigs in London. Wilhelm had the romantic's aversion to the intrusion of the intellect into the sphere of the emotions; his feeling for nature was outraged by facts and figures. He admired his brother's learning, his generosity and unselfishness; careful with his money, he was not a particularly generous man himself. Alexander, more tolerant perhaps, never criticized his brother, not even in his very unrestrained letters to Arago, of whom also he never said anything unkind or faintly malicious. They are the only two people who never became the target of his sarcastic wit. In spite of basic differences in temperament and principles, the two brothers were sincerely attached to each other and enjoyed the exchange of their interests and ideas. With all their gifts, they both disliked music, Wilhelm so much so that it caused him acute suffering; it was left to the good-hearted uncle to chaperon his nieces at concerts, a social calamity in his opinion, because their father roundly refused to do it.

As a member of the Berlin academy, Alexander was entitled to lecture at the university whenever he wished to do so. A few months after his return, he made use of this privilege to give a course on 'Physical Geography' which was open to the students and professors of all the faculties. It was his intention to demon-strate that it is possible to speak to the mind and the imagina-tion and yet to adhere to the scientific facts and so counter-balance the pernicious influence of the very popular philosophy of nature of that time. This natural philosophy, whose main exponents were Hegel and Schelling, was a misdirected attempt to understand natural phenomena intuitively and *a priori*. Experiments appeared to the practicians of this art as an act of violence, an interference with nature, and a mathematical formulation of natural laws, a procedure which destroyed man's feeling of awe and admiration in the face of natural pheno-mena. The natural philosophers in Germany were part of the romantic movement; they objected to any discipline which led to a divorce of the emotions from the intellect, and they tried to replace Newton's *principia mathematica* with sibylline sayings, some of them perfect gems of woolly-minded silliness. 'Granite is ether' or 'The diamond is a pebble which has acquired consciousness.' Schelling went particularly far in this anthro-pomorphic fatuousness. He believed or tried to bully his readers into believing that east is oxygen and west hydrogen; therefore, it rains when clouds from the west mix with clouds from the east. The forests are the hair of the earth animal, and the bulge in the equatorial region is the underbelly of nature. America has a feminine shape—on the atlas—long, slim, watery and icily cold at the 48th degree of latitude; the degrees of latitude are years; a woman becomes cold at the age of forty-eight. This man, professor of philosophy at the university of Berlin, had a large following among serious-minded people. It was quite courageous of Humboldt to try to open the eyes of men who kept them so obstinately closed. He never lost the eighteenth-century belief in the possibilities of education.

The lecture course on the physical description of the world began in November 1827 and lasted until the spring of 1828. The biggest lecture theatre in the university building over-flowed with professors and students, drawn from all the faculties; all the newspapers reported on it and it became so popular that Humboldt repeated the more general introductory cycle of about sixteen lectures in a concert hall for an audience of over a thousand people from all classes, male and female. The story goes that he had tried a similar venture for a small and select audience in the salon of Mme de Montauban in Paris in 1825 but nothing certain has ever been discovered about it; it seems to have been only too private. It is not unlikely that he modelled his course on the example of the Royal Institution. His attack on natural philosophy was in the main directed against Hegel, although he did not mention any names but voiced his objections against a natural philosophy without knowledge and experience. It was his policy to conduct scientific controversy on an impersonal basis. The public was very gently introduced to the unfamiliar subject by an initial survey of the history of science from the Greeks onwards and with special emphasis on the importance of the Arabic contribution. A discussion of the poetry of nature and of landscape painting served to lead his listeners from known ground to the stark facts of observation and experiment. The lectures were never published although he was urged by his German publisher Cotta to do so immediately and for a generous fee. Humboldt refused because he did not want to commit the spoken word to print without a complete revision. The course, however, formed the basis of his book *Cosmos*, which did not appear until nearly twenty years later. A short outline, which he had jotted down, came to light after his death. Apparently he talked about optics and interference phenomena, then the very latest subject, about the stars and the southern sky, the volcanoes on the moon, meteors and sun-spots. The more orthodox elements in the audience were not without anxiety for the possibly harmful effects on the mind of the public. Science, driven too far, seemed to them apt to lead to conflicts with religious tradition. Humboldt's account of the geological ages did not tally too well with the first chapter of Genesis. However, the musician Zelter reported to Goethe: 'I must now mention the great pleasure which Humboldt's mag-nificently rich colloquium on the miracles of nature gave me, a colloquium held in front of a most respectable audience of thousands. There is a man of my own kind who gives what he has, without grudge and without knowing to whom. He does not get any favours from it; there is no artifice, no mere wordiness. Even when he is wrong, it is a pleasure to believe him.'[1]

The presence of women was the sensation of the day. 'The hall could not cope with the audience and the female audience could not cope with the lectures,' said a would-be witty journalist, and the current joke was that one of his ardent listeners had ordered a new dress with sleeves of the width of two Sirius distances. When one of the royal princes asked Hum-boldt if he really believed that the ladies could follow, he replied: 'But that is quite unnecessary; if they only come, they do all that is possible.' It seems that the naturally superior intel-lect of men allowed every one of them perfect comprehension.

Humboldt had succeeded in making science socially accept-able in Berlin, a branch of knowledge, essential and comprehen-sible to the educated mind. In the same year, he also overcame the political prejudices of the authorities against scientific conferences; a large meeting of scientists and doctors was held in Berlin at which he presided together with M. Lichtenstein. The very first scientific congress had been organized by L. Oken in 1822; it had been convened in a beer cellar in Leip-zig, frowned upon by the political police. Since the Carlsbad Decisions, any kind of meeting was feared to lead to subversive talk and action; Oken himself was suspect as a liberal and came soon into active conflict with the authorities. When, two years after the Berlin meeting, the historians decided to organize similar conferences, Metternich became so alarmed that he sent a serious request to the Prussian government to prohibit the whole undertaking. No official action was taken but the Prussian historians were discreetly advised to stay away.

As president of the Berlin meeting, Humboldt had to give up a great deal of his time that summer to correspondence and organization; he was particularly delighted at the number of people who asked expressly that they should be found rooms without bed bugs. The Berliner variety was said to be un-commonly vicious. 'From the 18th to the 26th of September,' he wrote to Arago, 'we shall have an eruption of nomadic scientists; all the Danes and Swedes are coming, Berzelius and Oersted will be here on the 15th of August. I have no hope that even that might tempt you. However, there will be 400 great men and little doctors. I feel frightened and perfidious at the same time. The reception I shall have to give for them, will ruin me, but this rather silly affair is considered to be of national importance. I must appear to take it seriously.'[2] Six hundred members arrived in the end for the conference, among them Berzelius, Oersted and Gauss who stayed with Humboldt. Sabine and Babbage had both been invited, but only Babbage came. Humboldt ascribed Sabine's absence to the fact that Babbage had accepted for 'among two Englishmen there are always three who hate each other'. His organization of the meeting which, apart from a few general lectures, was divided up into sections for the special subjects, is the one still in use everywhere. At the opening session, at which the Prussian king and the Duke of Cumberland were present, Humboldt gave the opening address: 'The main purpose of this society is the personal contact of men who work in the same field, an oral and thus more stimulating exchange of ideas, they may be facts, opinions or doubts; the forming of friendly relations which light up the sciences, give charm to life and gentleness and tolerance to intercourse . . .', words which in one form or the other have since been endlessly repeated. The ruinous reception was given in the concert hall of the playhouse where tea and music were offered. The first meeting of the British Association in 1831 was modelled on the Berlin conference. Within the next ten years, Humboldt attended three more of these affairs but he soon wearied of them; in 1837 he writes to Gauss: 'I prefer a few hours with you to all sessions of the so-called scientists who move in such enormous numbers and so gastronomically that there is never enough scientific contact for me. In the end, I always ask myself like the mathematician after the opera: now tell me frankly what does that prove?'

The meeting was, however, not without consequences for Humboldt's own research; his discussions with other scientists, Gauss in particular, induced him to return to his observations of the fluctuations of the magnetic declination, observations which finally gave rise to the first international collaboration in science. This time, a specially constructed, non-magnetic hut in which all metal parts were made of copper, was set up in the garden of the house of Abraham Mendelssohn-Bartholdy. This was the eldest son of Moses Mendelssohn who had become a banker and a wealthy man with a patrician house and a patrician life. He was also the father of the composer Felix, then a young man of twenty and at the height of his powers. As Abraham ruefully remarked: 'As a young man I was the son of my father, and now I am the father of my son.' Humboldt's hut was in a corner of the garden, not far from the summer-house where Felix, Zelter's 'golden lad', and his older sister who was an accomplished musician herself, made music in the evenings and practised for the great musical event of the spring of 1829, the performance of the newly discovered St. Matthew's Passion, a hundred years after it had first been per- formed. And while the golden lads and girls rehearsed and laughed in the summer-house, the royal chamberlain and an army of helpers spent their days and nights in the little wooden building peering through a microscope at a black line on an ivory scale. One night, when Humboldt crept quietly to his observation post, the youngest member of the family, Rebecca, mistook him for a burglar and tried to chase him single-handed out of the garden before she discovered that he was the dis- tinguished friend of the family going about his lawful occasions. The long hours were shared by the astronomer Encke, the young mathematician Dirichlet, Dove, the meteorologist, and the physicist Poggendorf. Dirichlet met his fate in Rebecca Mendelssohn to whom he got married as soon as he had obtained a suitable academic post. Humboldt's recommenda- tions were instrumental in bringing about Dirichlet's appoint- ment to a professorship at the military college in Berlin.

The instrument used in these observations had been designed by Gambey. It consisted of a bar magnet suspended from a torsionless thread and carrying ivory scales on its two end faces. These scales could be observed through two travelling micro- scopes which were provided with cross-wires. In this way, it was possible to read either the figure on the cross-wires or dis- place the microscope until the zero of the magnet scale came back to the cross-wire, all this by the light of a candle. The shed was made draughtproof and kept at a constant tempera- ture to ensure that the magnet could not be set in motion by air currents. It probably was uncomfortably hot but that did not worry Humboldt. Ever since his return from the tropics, he had firmly kept the climate outside; a temperature of 70° in his rooms was quite usual. An unfortunate English geologist who had visited him in Paris, complained bitterly that he had caught pleurisy after staying in this hothouse atmosphere on a very cold winter's day.

At the time, Humboldt met with very little enthusiasm among other scientists for his observations. It was the general opinion that they were rather a waste of time since it did not seem possible to disentangle the various effects responsible for the small and irregular fluctuations of the magnet. From the beginning, his special interest was directed towards simul‑ taneous observations in different places; in this way, it could be decided whether the position of the sun had an influence on the variations or whether they were of purely terrestrial origin. Readings were therefore taken simultaneously in Paris, Berlin and in a mine in Freiberg in Saxony, thirty‑five fathoms under‑ ground. It was soon discovered that magnetic storms occurred even when no aurorae were visible. It must be emphasized that these experiments were concerned with the regular hourly variations as well as with the irregular storms. The collabora‑ tion between Berlin and Freiberg proved that the daily varia‑ tions in the mine agreed with those obtained above ground although the fluctuations of the temperature do not penetrate so far into the earth. A possible reason for the effect was then sought in the position of the sun: 'I think that the daily variation from maximum to minimum depends on the altitude of the sun at every locality; but if there is a movement at night in the interior of the earth, this cause which would act simultaneously, should be influenced in the effects by the longitude. If simul‑ taneous observations were made for several days at different seasons, it should be possible to distinguish between such effects. I am again surprised at these great agitations which set the magnet into oscillations over 15 to 18 minutes of arc with‑ out a change in the average value. What is this lateral force which acts suddenly or gradually on the formerly stationary needle, and which vanishes again since it does not affect the average value?'[3] Arago was inclined to ascribe these rapid oscillations to air currents but this idea was disposed of by the fact that they occurred in a draughtproof hut, as Humboldt pointed out: 'If the agreement of these perturbations is found to depend on the distance from *noon*, the change of the per-turbations is, so to speak, an *affection* which the course of the sun (as in the hourly variations) has on certain days for the magnetic charge of the crust of the earth.'[3] The periodic measurements of the variation of the magnetic declination were carried on in the Mendelssohn garden until Abraham's death when the place was sold. They were then continued in the new observatory with a greatly improved instrument, following Gauss's design.

In the middle of his magnetic preoccupations, Humboldt was deep in preparations for his journey to Siberia. From the moment of his return from America, he had never abandoned his plans for a second expedition, preferably to Asia. But he had to wait twenty-four years before the circumstances allowed a realization of his dreams. After travelling in the Andes, he was irresistibly attracted by the idea of climbing in the Hima-layas. As early as 1805, he talked vaguely of plans to go to the Missouri, the North Pole, or Asia, as soon as he had finished his books on the American expedition. In 1811, success seemed very near. The Russian minister Romanoff had invited him to accompany a mission to Kashgar and Tibet. Humboldt had completed all his preparations and gone to Vienna to say good-bye to his brother who was at that time Prussian envoy in Austria, when Napoleon, as once before, disposed of his plans by invading Russia. Humboldt returned to Paris, started to learn Persian and decided to travel at his own expense through Persia and Afghanistan to India. Instead he had to sit out the wars in Paris. Three years after Waterloo, Frederick William III offered him an annual grant of £1,800 and the cost of the equipment for a journey to India; again, the plan came to nothing for unknown reasons, although there are vague hints that the East India Company had indicated that it would not relish a visit from a foreign traveller. Humboldt's thoughts began now to turn to Mexico where he could expect to be welcome. He played with the idea of founding a research institute in Mexico City and of surrounding himself with young and enthusiastic scientists.

His final chance came about in an unexpected manner. The Russian platinum mines had produced a very large harvest of this new metal, and the government was looking for some means of utilization. It was considered too unattractive for decorative purposes; it was mainly employed in the manufacture of huge crucibles for industrial furnaces. Although it shared with gold and silver the resistance to corrosion and chemical reactions, its dull colour and comparative lack of metallic brilliance precluded it from attaining the rank of a precious metal. The Spanish government which had found itself in the same embarrassment as a result of the exploitation of the Gran Chaco mines, had consulted Humboldt, soon after his return from Mexico, on the advisability of a platinum currency. His advice was unfavourable to the idea since there was no fixed market price such as existed for the other precious metals. The plan was thereupon dropped but revived by Bolívar after the rebellion of the South American states; he even sent a representative to the Vienna Congress who pleaded with the Allies to recognize the value of an eventual platinum currency. He failed but Bolívar went ahead with a coin for purely internal consumption; the necessary legislation was introduced in Colombia in the spring of 1826. The price of platinum was at that time about five times that of silver and a third of that of gold. The Russian government began now seriously to consider this possibility and the finance minister, Count Cancrin, a progressive and liberal minded man, consulted in his turn Humboldt in the autumn of 1827 on his opinions about the matter.

The occurrence of platinum in the northern Ural [he wrote] is by no means unimportant. It is, however, difficult to sell; no great amount is dug and refined, and there is even less promise for the future.

I have therefore considered minting a platinum coin such as is projected in Colombia, a kind of luxury coin for voluntary circulation for which a market might also be found in Europe. There are no technical or economic difficulties or delays but two other points arise:

(1) the indistinguishability between platinum and silver for less practised eyes;
(2) the uncertain value of the metal.

To overcome the first disadvantage, I have thought of striking a coin with the weight of the silver rouble or half a silver rouble but half their size. In that case, the difference in specific weight becomes so obvious that a deception will be difficult. The problem of the relative value appears more difficult; platinum has none of the attractive qualities of gold and silver; it is not easy to work and has not yet found many applications. There is no real necessity for its use and it does not exist in any quantity. A stable price, if it is attained, cannot be expected to be high. The value is not determined by the scarcity of a commodity but by its usefulness or beauty.

I have collected some information about the price of platinum in England and France which seems to indicate that on the average an ounce of unrefined platinum costs six shillings and more, it costs twenty-five shillings if completely refined.

Even if this is accurate, it does not help much to determine the value of the coin since the price of the metal will fall when the quantity increases. I do not feel inclined, however, to worry too much because the value of the coin, once established, may lead to a stabilisation of the price of platinum or at least to a closer definition. [4]

The letter was accompanied by several medals and samples of the newly minted platinum coins together with the corresponding silver roubles. After the death of Humboldt, these specimens were bought back from the heirs and incorporated in the numismatic collection of the Hermitage.

Humboldt strongly advised Cancrin against the introduction of a platinum coin; the price of the metal on the world market was, according to his information, entirely dependent on the general economic situation.

Since Your Excellency expects a frank statement from me, I must confess that any minting of platinum coins still appears unwise to me. There is nowadays so much intercourse between nations in both hemi- spheres that the possibility of a provincial coin in the strict meaning of the word no longer exists. An immense empire like that which enjoys the economic activity of Your Excellency, is certainly more than any other suitable for an experiment with a provincial coin: but what country is now cut off like an island? If the perplexing rate of silver to platinum is not recognised by the other Baltic states, by England, Holland and France, it will be difficult to ensure the coin a circulation in the interior of Russia at a stable price.

The difficulty in enforcing, after thousands of years, the use of a new metal as a representative and easy means of exchange, arises not alone from the necessity to overcome the habit of the people but even more from the fact that gold and silver find extensive application outside the monetary system.

Compared with these older metals, the employment of platinum in utensils is inconsiderable; there is little hope that its cold, unpleasant colour will permit an increased demand for platinum as an article of fashion, in spite of other excellent qualifications. This lack of applica- bility, minting apart, produces price fluctuations of 30 to 40 per cent as soon as even small quantities from Colombia, Brazil and the Urals come on the European markets. I feel doubtful therefore whether it will be possible to expect a stable value or at any rate an oscillation between narrow limits since the use of this metal is so very restricted. Should a free, active and more rational exploitation of the South American mines lead to a considerable increase of the annual produce of gold and silver and a consequent lowering of the value of these metals, as means of exchange, this diminution would soon reach a limit through the intensi- fied use for other purposes. This limiting value, this recovery of the equilibrium will never be attained by platinum, or so I fear. Produced and minted in great quantity, almost completely excluded from manu- facture, platinum, amassed as coin in one country, would become a kind of heavy, inconvenient paper currency, and the well intended aim to help the mine owners would not be reached at all.

A Russian platinum coin would indeed modify the price of platinum on the world market, but cannot be finally decisive. This determination depends on the demand and supply. In as much as the world of commerce can effect payments in Russia with platinum, the world market price will be determined by the rate of payment. Should the demand fall, the price at which Russia has sent the new metal into circulation will unfortunately fall with it.[5]

Since advice, even that of scientific experts, is heeded only where it encourages, Cancrin went ahead with his plans for the minting of a limited amount of platinum coins; the first pieces to the value of three silver roubles appeared in 1828, followed by six and even twelve roubles in the next two years, with a corresponding revival of mining activities. Experiments were also made with the production of platinum steel which is comparatively rust-free but proved in the end to be too costly. The coins, which had never been legal tender, had to be with-drawn in 1845 as the price for platinum on the world market had by then fallen to 55 per cent of the nominal value. The whole project was discussed again when, from 1857 onwards, the price took a definite upward trend, but it was finally rejected in 1863 with a resolution which echoes the doubts expressed by Humboldt in 1827: 'In spite of certain natural advantages for the use of platinum in a minted coin, it must not be overlooked that it lacks many other properties which, in the aggregate, enable gold and silver to serve as means of exchange and to assume the character of a universally valid coin. With the lack of a general demand for platinum, with the impossibility of fixing a universally valid price for it, a coin minted of this metal will never have more than a relative importance and a conditional value, and that only in very narrow limits, inasmuch as it could only circulate on condition that it will be accepted by the treasury.'[6]

In his very first reply to Cancrin, Humboldt had taken the opportunity to indicate his wish to wait upon the Czar in person and to satisfy his old dream of seeing the Urals and Lake Baykal. The delicate hint was immediately taken up: Cancrin invited him to make an inspection of the mines in the Ural mountains at the expense of the Russian government, and early in 1828, Humboldt accepted this offer. He proposed to start on his journey in the spring of 1829 as he did not wish to leave before the account of the American travels had been completely published and before he had carried out his intention to give his lecture course on geophysics in Berlin. There was another and sadder reason for his refusal to go just then: Caroline, his brother's wife, suffered from cancer and he wanted to remain near Wilhelm as long as she was alive.

The journey, planned to last only one summer, was not, strictly speaking, a real expedition, but an excursion to study mining and geology in the Urals with possibly a visit to western Siberia. 'I always talk of Tobolsk for I implore His Imperial Majesty for the permission to let me go to the Irtysh at least (Rubtsovsk is presumably too far for one summer). Tobolsk is a dream of my youth. . . . I have a childish aversion from the cold but know how to live for a higher purpose.'[7] Humboldt initially proposed to travel from St. Petersburg via Gorkiy, Kazan, Chkalov, Sverdlovsk and Tyumen to Tobolsk and to return through Kurgan, Ufa, Kuybyshev to Moscow. The necessity for a discussion of the finances of the expedition caused him some embarrassment: 'I come now with some feeling of shame to the very prosaic point which Your Excellency has requested me to touch quite freely. What I find permissible to accept, depends entirely on how far you think I can be useful to the government. This usefulness is in my opinion very limited; I shall always believe that I have received and given nothing in return. I shall be immeasurably rewarded for the physical effort and the inevitable boredom of the mono⁄tonous sight of large plains if I can be in the open air for five to six months, see the magnificent mountain strata of the Urals (sapphire rocks) and a lively, vigorous nation and enjoy the progressive civilization. I have spent everything I had inherited (£15,000) and since I have sacrificed it to scientific purposes, I say it without fear of being blamed. The king who employs me in a purely personal capacity, pays me more generously than my services as a scientist and consultant in a few administrative affairs deserve, £750 a year. Since I am a very poor manager and since I like to help young students, I have until now spent more every year than I possess; I am therefore forced to hope that the Irtysh waters will not on my return to Berlin or Paris, worsen the situation and plunge me into a serious financial confusion. I cannot express myself more frankly and openly to a minister of state; I may do it as in both continents I have never been regarded as politically ambitious or greedy for money. When Your Excellency in your letter of the 8/20th of March of the last year, told me of the gracious interest of the noble monarch, you used yourself the expression: the cost of the journey will be met by the imperial treasury. I should prefer not to spend more than £375 to £450 until my return to Berlin. This will cover little more than the cost of the journey from Berlin to Petersburg and from Moscow to Berlin or Paris on the return; any expense above that, i.e. the amount by which I overspend, I beg you to return to me from the treasury. I have no wish to improve my situation in any way but should like to avoid finding myself more embarrassed as a result of this journey. With the confidence which Your Excellency has for me, you will not demand a detailed account of the cost; therefore, it would be simplest for you, the giver, and for me, the receiver, if you permitted that I may tell you when I leave Russia again in the autumn, by how much the total I have spent, exceeds the small sum I can contribute myself. I shall travel in my own French carriage which can be closed in front with glass, with *one* German servant (a rifleman, for the sake of whose health I want to provide some comfort), and with the professor of chemistry and mineralogy Gustav Rose, a young, modest and instructed man. We shall therefore be three people to start with; to take more, seemed to me immodest. I am fond of comfort, in particular cleanliness where it is obtainable, but am cheerful and contented in privation when it is necessary. I am indifferent towards treatment as a person of rank but very grateful for kindness.'[8]

Politically, the prospect of a journey through Russia was not without embarrassment for Humboldt. It was generally known that his opinions were violently opposed to the suppression of freedom of expression and the state of subjection of the peasants practised by the Russian régime, just as he had been opposed to the ruthless isolation and the slavery of Negroes in South America. He had given indignant expression to his feelings in his *Political Essay on the Island of Cuba*: 'It is the duty of the traveller who has seen the torments and degradations of human nature, to bring the accusations of the unfortunate to the notice of those whose task it is to procure their relief.' At that time, he had travelled at his own expense; he had also been twenty years younger. Now, his position at the Prussian court and his sense of obligation towards the Czar made it imperative for him to abstain from any political comments. He gave a delicately worded assurance to Cancrin that he and his companions would confine themselves to observations of the nature of the country and that they would refrain from any comments on public institutions and the situation of the lower classes.

Nevertheless, the inspection of the mines in the Urals and Siberia suggested some reforms to Humboldt which he put before Cancrin after his return. He could, with perfect justice, demonstrate that the distribution of labour which was based on the situation of the lower classes, rendered the mines un-economical; the number of people in actual use for their operation was many times greater than in England and Germany. The main obstacle was the lack of specialization of the workmen; one and the same man had to be proficient in timber-felling, metal-casting and gold-panning, for the simple reason that work in the mines and smelting works was compulsory for the peasants. Humboldt proposed that the Crown should remedy this lack of trained labour by settling free skilled workmen on land in its possession. Cancrin made these ideas the basis of an outline law which he sent to the director of the Ural mines for his opinion. He wanted to settle free men of all classes, in particular mining officials and various workmen on the land to increase the cultivation of the districts and to augment the size of the available labour force. The small holdings were intended to be tax-free for six years and to become eventually hereditary. Every labourer was to have a piece of cultivable ground near his house, rent-free and equally to be handed on from father to son. The number of towns was to be enlarged with a corresponding increase in industry. He considered it particularly desirable to introduce industries for the employment of women who 'lived in complete idleness in the Ural'. The reply of the mining director was very negative. The proposal of introducing free farmers and workmen into the district alarmed the private owners of the region; the counter proposal that retired mining officials should be given land on which they were entitled, as members of the nobility, to settle serfs, indicated the reluctance for any change in the system. The correspondence between the finance ministry and the mining authorities about the necessary reforms of the organization lasted for decades; it was impossible to enforce any action until the emancipation of the serfs in 1861 when the miners and foundry workers were also released from forced labour.

Ten

EXPEDITION TO SIBERIA

CAROLINE HUMBOLDT died in March 1829, and on the 12th of April Humboldt, accompanied by Rose and the equally youthful zoologist Ehrenberg, who in all modesty had been added to the party, set out on their long journey across the continent. This time, the reputation of the traveller preceded him; receptions, banquets and speeches rained on him at every stop, and he grew heartily weary of them.

It was early in the year for such a tour in eastern Europe; the rivers were just breaking through their crust of ice and the floods caused many delays. On the way to St. Petersburg, the carriages were ferried across the swollen rivers on rafts; no mis-hap occurred on the twenty-three crossings and none of the instruments suffered any damage. Their way lay along the Bal-tic coast of the former East Prussia, famed for its amber. It is in the main collected on the shore but in certain places which are distinguished by a soil of fine bluish clay, it is dug out of the ground. The exploitation was in the hands of a Scotsman who held the concession from the Prussian crown, and who showed Humboldt's party his stocks of the lovely fossilized resin. The accounts, which existed since the sixteenth century, show that the supply is remarkably constant. For the inhabitants of the district, the search for amber imposed uncomfortable restric-tions on their life. A day by the sea meant a search by coast-guards in the evening, unless they kept to a small resort in the dreariest part of the coast, and the fishermen were forced to use only certain specified harbours, away from the main mining localities.

The route followed the line of the shore along the Kurish

Nehrung, a sandy spit of land between an inner lagoon and the sea, a formation which occurs again on the southern coast of France between Montpellier and the Pyrenees and on the Adriatic coast of Italy, the coasts of an equally tideless sea. A ridge of dunes separated the villages in the east from the open sea in the west, where a double line of trees was the only indica/ tion of the road; the drivers preferred the damp sand just above the water line for the sake of their horses. The ice floes which a strong wind had piled up in the narrow opening between the lagoon and the sea, made the crossing to Memel (Klaipéda) impossible and Humboldt used the enforced stay in a small country inn to make magnetic observations. 'The scenery con/ sists of a ploughed field, three birches and two pines; it sweeps along towards the north/east with a charming uniformity for two hundred and twenty miles. . . . The most characteristic fea/ ture of this unnatural nature which I have seen, is the Nehrung where we stayed for four to five days and which yielded five shells and three lichens. If Schinkel would stick a few bricks together there, if a Monday circle, a circle of artistic Jewish ladies and an academy could be established on these sandy steppes which are covered with shrubs, it would be all that is needed to found a new Berlin. Indeed, I should prefer the new creation for I have seen the sun set in splendour over the Neh/ rung. And also, as you know, the people here speak pure San/ skrit: Lithuanian. . . . It would be wearying to speak of Tartu and the celebrations there: university equipage with four horses, professorial visits from 8 o'clock in the morning until 9 o'clock at night, a splendid dinner given by the whole university with obbligato toasts, side by side with interesting people and interest/ ing sights (above all Struve with his 2,000 double stars and the wonderful telescope). A blizzard which has plagued us for three days, has made any observation of the sky impossible but by repeated experiments I have convinced myself that I can read the micrometer with an error of less than 1/30 second. In Riga, we were met by a mail courier who rides in front now and gives us such a prosperous air that we have to pay 60 to 70 shillings for one night. On these bottomless roads we need 12 horses (for both carriages) as against 6 to 8 before. The whole journey to St. Petersburg will easily cost £360 (still £140 below the £500 I have been given). The courier says, a journey with 400 horses costs here £55 to £60.'[1]

The reception given to Humboldt in St. Petersburg was truly princely: nearly every day, he dined with the Czar, Nicholas I, whose wife was a daughter of the Prussian king, and his family. Everybody who was somebody called and tried to press more hospitality on him. The departmental chiefs were put at his disposal, and he was offered money like hay from official sources. Exhausted with the never-ending necessity for representation and the pressure of the curious, he longed for the moment when he could escape into the open country, far from the towns and the boredom of fame.

The long drive through the great Russian plains was conducted by highly placed mining officials and preceded by the dignitaries of the provincial administration; the whole caravan sometimes needed thirty to forty horses at every stage. The scenery was disappointingly similar to what they had left behind, but the villages with their blockhouses and their streets paved with wooden blocks were strange. A large sailing boat took them down the Volga, from Gorkiy to Kazan. Compared with the journey on the Orinoco, this was luxury indeed. The carriages were taken on board; a table and benches under a sailcloth awning in the centre of the ship provided accommodation for the party. There was a brick stove for the preparation of the meals and the provisions filled a small boat which was towed behind. Although the wind was against them and the four men at the oars had to row the whole way, the journey with the current was reasonably fast, and they reached Kazan with its lively university in three days. After a visit to a nearby Mohammedan village with 'eleven mosques', the first Humboldt had ever seen, they reached the slopes of the Urals in June, on good gravelled roads, nearly as good as English roads. Everywhere they were pursued by visits from 'men with swords'. It was the Orinoco with epaulettes.

With the arrival of the party at Sverdlovsk, began the real object of the journey, the study of the enormously rich mines of the Urals; iron and copper, malachite, beryl and topaz and above all the gold and platinum deposits engaged the former mining inspector's particular attention. For a month, he travelled in the mountains, often the whole day on foot; many times they did not reach the pits until the evening and descended into the workings as late as nine o'clock at night. He went everywhere in a dark-brown tail coat, a white cravat round his neck and a round hat on his head. In his sixtieth year, he was as good a mountaineer as in the Andes and completely surefooted over boulders and scree. The formation of the Ural mountains, which consist of roughly parallel chains aligned along the direction of a meridian, reminded him of the cordilleras of South America, although the heights of the peaks, which do not reach above 6,200 feet, seemed very modest by comparison with the American and Indian giants.

Towards the end of July, they left the mountains behind and at last entered Siberia. Humboldt's youthful dream came true; he stayed for a few days in Tobolsk, in the house of a German doctor who, to prove that the world was a small place even then, turned out to be the son of Werther's Lotte. Siberian 'long carriages', in which the traveller rides stretched out on the bottom, brought them through the steppe of Barabinsk and Barnaul to the frontier of Chinese Dzungaria. The mosquitoes were at the height of their powers; they pursued their means of livelihood even to the bottom of the mines. Following the local custom, everybody sweated under a mask, a kind of leather helmet with a neck covering and closed in front by a horsehair net. As the shops in Tobolsk did not have them in stock, they had to be improvised from the operative parts of hair sieves. The steppe between Tobolsk and Ust-Kamenogorsk was then scarcely populated; small villages at every stage of the road provided the horses. But it was not as dry and arid as Humboldt had imagined it; the ground was covered with lakes of various sizes; small rivers and swamps or marshes, many of them salty, a typical feature of Central Asia, moisten the soil which is lush with grass and herbs. Poplars, birches and clumps of huge delphiniums give the country the character of a park where the dry stalks of tulips and iris recall the glories of springtime. The villages were unhealthy places at that time of the year; an epidemic of typhus was raging, presumably caused by the unhygienic habit of the people of surrounding the hamlets with a wall of dung. To avoid all contact with the sick, the party travelled day and night; in this way they made remarkably quick progress and travelled nearly 1,000 miles in nine days. 'You will have seen from my letter from Tobolsk that we have taken the bold decision to visit the most important part of the Altay, an excursion of more than 1,800 miles of which we finished to-day 920 miles (the distance from Berlin to St. Petersburg). We travel or rather fly through these monotonous Siberian grass regions as through a sea—a veritable cruise on land on which we make 160 to 180 miles in 24 hours. From Tobolsk to Tara, we did not suffer much; but in Kainsk and the steppe of Barabinsk, we suffered a great deal from dust, heat and yellow midges (one kind of them won in the end). This plague is not much worse on the Orinoco, and although the thermometer is only 86° in the shade, we suffer from the heat because of the contrast with the cold nights (43°). The 24th of July, we were in the beautifully situated monastery Abalak on the Irtysh, above Tobolsk, the 29th in Kainsk, the 31st we saw the majestic Ob for the first time and crossed it at Berdsk. We found much illness in the villages where sometimes as many as 4 to 5 people died every day (typhus). But since we travelled day and night, we arrived in good health on the morning of the 1st of August in the district of the mountain town Barnaul of the Altay (as far to the east of Berlin as Caracas is to the west), on the banks of the Ob which has many bends here. A SSW gale from the Kirghiz steppe raged for seventeen hours: the Ob had waves like the sea and it was impossible to cross. We all camped during the night on the bank of the river. The flames, rising high in the forest, reminded me of the Orinoco. Rain and gales alternated, on the whole a blessing since we were now rid of the mosquitoes and did not need the suffocating masks any more. At two o'clock in the morning, we were able to cross and have enjoyed two pleasant days here in Barnaul where 17 tons of silver are cast and where the president of the province of Tobolsk has brought together a beautiful collection of Chinese, Mongolian and Tibetan manuscripts. The great and all too benevolent care of the government unfortunately leads to a daily increase in the number of our companions. . . . The vegetation has at last become Siberian, now we have penetrated 2,300 miles into Asia; however, the banks of the Ob resemble on the whole the Havel and the lake of Tegel since the trees alone determine the character of a country. About the larger animals I will only say that big tigers, striped just like the Bengal tiger, have been seen in these northern latitudes. We have seen the pelts of two such animals and shall buy them for the zoological cabinet in Berlin. The existence of these beasts so far north is very, very strange.'[2] The high light of the journey was a visit to the frontier post of Chinese Dzungaria north of Lake Zaysan, now part of Russian Kazakhstan. Two encampments, miserable tents manned by tattered Mongol soldiers, guarded the banks of the Irtysh. Camels grazed in the valley, overlooked by a small Chinese temple on an arid hill. The majesty of the distant Chinese empire was represented by the polished manners of the commandants. Humboldt was enchanted with their decorative silk dress and the peacock feather in their caps. The real importance of the journey through the Altay lay for him, however, in the sight of a mass of granite which had pushed its way through a bed of slate and had visibly poured over the rocks in uninterrupted flow, one more proof of its eruptive nature.

They returned by boat on the Irtysh to Omsk where the Cossack college gave them a reception with speeches in Tartar, Mongol and Russian, all of these languages being completely incomprehensible to Humboldt for all the efforts he had made to learn at least Russian. Returned to Chkalov, Humboldt could not resist the temptation to pay a visit to the Caspian Sea in order to study its fish and the chemical composition of this inland ocean. The country between the Ural and the lower Volga was still true steppe, very arid in the late summer, poor in flora and fauna. A few scattered herds of small antelopes were sometimes seen in the distance; poisonous scorpions and the sinister spider which the Kalmucks have named the black widow—it first became known in Europe through this expedi- tion—had to be avoided. A number of lakes, salt-encrusted and shallow, provided the salt which preserves sturgeon and caviare on its long journeys. Astrakhan fascinated Humboldt by the mixture of Russians, Tartars who were skilled artisans, mostly dyers and tanners, Kalmucks from the steppe, Mongol cara- vans from Central Asia, Persians, Indians and a prosperous colony of Armenian merchants who had their quarters and their places of religious worship in the town. They cruised in a steam launch on the Caspian Sea, and Rose collected his samples while Humboldt took readings on the barometer to connect the level of Chkalov and Kazan to that of the Caspian basin which the scientists E. K. Hofmann and Gregor von Helmersen had discovered to be below sea level. At that time four steamboats were in use in Astrakhan; they served to pilot the sailing ships into the harbour. Since there was no coal in the immediate neighbourhood, the boilers were fired with wood; the fuel was stored on boats which were towed behind the launches. The difficulty of transporting enough wood for longer journeys prevented Humboldt from going to Baku to see the petroleum wells with his own eyes.

137

Throughout the expedition, Rose and Ehrenberg had respectively carried out geological, zoological and botanical observations while Humboldt had been occupied with the climatological and magnetic measurements. He carried a number of thermometers, two of which had been calibrated by GayLussac and Bessel; a large alcohol thermometer, specially designed by GayLussac for recording low temperatures, was deposited in Tobolsk for future observations. For the magnetic measurements, Humboldt had been provided with a nonmagnetic tent, with copper in all metallic parts, which he set up away from towns, He had a large magnetometer, made by Gambey, with which he could observe the dip and the period of oscillation of the magnet.

Towards the end of October 1829, the party turned back, and it arrived in Moscow at the beginning of November. Nobody had been ill; only the poor horses had several times collapsed in the heat. The Cossack postboys, whose foolhardiness had been everything expected from a Cossack, had often fallen from the coaches; but they fell like trained commandos and rolled laughing out between the rear wheels. None of the carriages had overturned or broken down.

The arrival of the travellers in Moscow started off a new series of receptions; a special meeting of the Moscow scientific society was held at which Rose and Ehrenberg were invited to discuss the results of the expedition. Alexander Herzen, at that time a student of the university, was present at this occasion and has left a report of it: 'On his return from the Urals, Humboldt was received at a solemn meeting of the scientific society, then in existence at the university of Moscow; to this society belonged several senators, governors, generals, etc., in short people who had never occupied themselves with the sciences or any other branch of knowledge. The reputation of Humboldt, privy councillor of his majesty the king of Prussia, on whom the Czar had conferred the order of St. Anne, had penetrated even to them, and they had decided to make their obeisance to the man who had climbed Chimborazo and who had stayed at Sanssouci.'

'They took the affair very seriously; the governor general, the military and civil dignitaries appeared in gala uniform with orders and decorations; the professors marched about with their three-cornered hats under the arm, dragging a martial sword. Humboldt, who had not expected anything like this, arrived in a simple blue coat and looked very embarrassed. Seats had been put in the passage from the staircase to the hall where the 'scientists' usually met; here stood the rector, there a dean, on the right a professor at the beginning of his career, on the left a veteran who was at the end and perhaps for that reason spoke so very slowly. Every one of them delivered a speech, one in German, the other in Latin, the third in French, and all that in passages where no one could stay for a minute without catching a cold lasting for months. Humboldt listened patiently to all these harangues, hat in hand, and replied to every one—I believe that all the coloured and not quite so coloured savages among whom he had lived, cannot have caused the great explorer so much discomfort as the celebrations at the Moscow reception.'

'When at last he entered the hall and took his seat, the whole audience stood up solemnly. The curator of the university, Pissarev, had thought it necessary to read a sort of order of the day on the merits of his excellency, the great traveller, in the traditional style and in Russian. After that, Sergey Glinka declaimed in his hoarse soldier's voice a poem which began with the words: 'Humboldt, Prometheus of our days!'

'And Humboldt had had the intention to discuss his obser-vations of the magnetic declination, to put his meteorological measurements, made in the Urals, before the Moscow scien-tists. Instead, he was shown by the rector some braiding done with the illustrious hair of Peter the Great. Only with the greatest difficulty could his companions, Ehrenberg and Rose, find the moment to talk about their discoveries.'[3]

On the 13th of November they were back in St. Petersburg; in six months they had covered 12,000 miles. Humboldt's first concern was to return to Cancrin the money which he had managed to bring back out of the initial grant. From the beginning of the journey, he had planned to save half of the remittance of £1,000 given to him on his departure. As usual, his budgeting had been overoptimistic; also, the expedition had been extended beyond the limits originally intended, and the number of persons in the party had continually been increased. There was, too, what he termed 'his lack of skill in keeping down minor expenditure', or more bluntly his habit of overtipping, so that in the end £375 were left to be handed over. Cancrin must have been somewhat surprised at this gesture since he had seen the original sum as a payment on account only, but he accepted it, and made it immediately available for a journey of Hofmann and Helmersen, the two scientists who had attached themselves to Humboldt's party in Siberia.

A special session of the academy had been convened at St. Petersburg at which Humboldt had to read a discourse, an ordeal by which he pretended to be frightened, although talking came as easily to him as breathing. Pushkin is supposed to have said of him that he resembled the marble lions of a fountain: he spouted brilliant talk as they spout water. Still, he intended to use this opportunity to make an impact on scientific organization; it was not only one of the greatest days in his life but a day of supreme importance in the development of meteorology and geophysics.

After an introduction in which Humboldt discussed the scientific projects and discoveries produced in Russia during the preceding year—his manners were always impeccable—he went on to suggest the organization of a network of stations in the European and Asiatic possessions of Russia for the purpose of meteorological and magnetic observations which would be of material as well as scientific benefit. The vast extent of the country, larger than the visible part of the moon, made such an enterprise particularly suitable; the academy seemed to him the right centre for such an organization. He proposed that these stations should stretch from St. Petersburg to Kyakhta and that continuous observations of the magnetic inclination, declination and intensity should be carried out. The meteorological measurements were to be taken hourly; they should include barometric readings, determinations of the atmospheric temperature and humidity and the amount of rainfall, all of them of the greatest importance for agriculture and communications. He pointed to the example of the United States which already possessed such a network, where observations were made with standardized instruments, and the statistical data obtained published by a central committee. It seemed to him advisable to set up an institute in St. Petersburg at which the calibration of the necessary instruments could be carried out. His lecture proved to be as successful as he had hoped; a committee under Count Cancrin and Professor Kupffer, whose observations of magnetic storms at the University of Kazan had proved the simultaneity of these perturbations over a great part of Europe, made an immediate start on the organization; by 1835 a number of meteorological and magnetic stations, stretching from St. Petersburg to Peking, had begun to collect data. It took only five years to build, staff and equip more than a dozen institutes, including one off the coast of Alaska, in a country which was notorious for bureaucratic procrastination, an impressive testimonial to the vigour of its scientists. Acting upon Humboldt's advice, observations were made with identical instruments of the magnetic dip and declination, the barometric pressure, temperature and humidity of the air, the direction of winds and the amount of rain- and snow-fall.

With the establishment of this collaboration, proposals came to fruition which had originally been made by Leibniz to the Czar Peter the Great, as Humboldt himself pointed out. The two men had had a discussion in Torgau in 1712 and Leibniz's ideas are preserved in a letter to the Czar:

Since Your Majesty condescended to let me know at *Torgau* that my proposals did not displease, I have not failed to have a magnetic globe made, unique of its kind, and spreading a new light on navigation. If it were made compulsory to furnish new observations every ten years, and if new globes were constructed with these results and employed in the practice of navigation, a quantity would without doubt be obtained which, for every interval of ten years, could serve for longitudes, i.e. which the Dutch call (the knowledge of) east and west. If this work were several times renewed, one would in the end succeed in discovering a fixed and permanent point of departure (i.e. general laws). Now, since the magnet has not only a declination in the horizontal plane but also an inclination in the vertical plane, it is of the utmost necessity to observe the latter carefully. I have built a special apparatus for this purpose (*instrumentum inclinationis*), and I maintain that it would be desirable that the declination and inclination should be observed at many localities and at different periods in the vast empire of Your Majesty, which observa- tions would be of the greatest usefulness for the navy. I await with interest the publication of the order which Your Majesty has deigned to promise me to that effect. For the details of the operations, I refer to the proposals which I have dared to submit at Torgau. I hope that in spite of the calamities of war, Your Majesty will find the time (the most invaluable thing among all we possess) to organise the researches and to obtain without major expense great results, useful for the progress and the aggrandisement of the domain of science and the arts. Examining an extract of letters received from Cathay which I have the honour to com- municate to Your Majesty, Your Majesty will see with some satisfaction that there also the sciences are cultivated. Your Majesty will be the link between Europe and China. [4]

Preoccupied with his campaigns and social reforms, Peter never found the time to carry out Leibniz's plans; they had been buried in the Russian archives until Humboldt resurrected them during his stay in Moscow.

Overwhelmed with parting gifts, among them a fur-lined coat and a seven-foot high malachite vase, Humboldt and his companions left St. Petersburg at the beginning of December and reached Berlin again at the end of the month. All the time he had been away, he had been longing for a letter from Arago;

at last, he found one waiting for him in Berlin with the news that his friend's wife, who had for some time been suffering from tuberculosis, had died.

Here I am back in Germany, and on the evening of my arrival I find your letter, dear friend, whose every line has torn my heart. I thank you from the bottom of my heart for the vivid and frank expression of the pain which had overwhelmed you in the last six months. It is an honour for me, it is the recognition that nobody on earth has been so devoted to you as I have been, because nobody has understood you, nobody has appreciated like me the strength of your character, the goodness of your heart and your intellectual powers. This attachment, this cult of my friendship for you, for Mme. Arago, for everything that is yours, has never grown less for an instant; it has been the happiness of my life when I was fortunate enough to live in Paris, it has nourished my imagination since circumstances, my position with the king of Prussia and (I can confess it now that I have safely returned from a journey of 10,000 miles) the hope of ending my career with a new enterprise have cast me on this desert beach. Can I be thankful for the ignorance during my expedition to Siberia and the Caspian Sea, far away from newspapers, meeting in St. Petersburg only travellers who frequent the more frivolous sections of Parisian society? This dreadful news, my fear for your health would have overwhelmed me in my activities. Valenciennes' stay in Berlin had left me some hope, and this hope was a comfort to me every time I thought of you, dear friend. But can you believe it, the dreadful news did not reach me until the 25th of December in Königsberg where I saw the Jewish geometrician Jacobi, the adored idol of Legendre before he recognised all the worth of Abel who fell a victim to the same disease as Malus, Petit and all those we shall mourn for the rest of our days.

This death which has shattered your existence, is for that very reason one of the greatest events in my life because I have lost with her all that the affection of a woman endowed with eminent qualities could give to the best, the most constant friend of her home. Such vivacity and such natural spirits. Such a seductive mixture of energy and sensibility, of intellect and imagination! What self-control at the approach of a separation when she thought only of you. I am proud that she remembered me in this cruel moment, that she called me the best of friends; my tears have fallen on this sheet; I shall make you cry but I do not regret it; the only peace is in this painful memory. No distraction is possible in such a situation; my brother whose pain is equally vivid, has retired for the winter to the country (to Tegel) where I shall go every week to see him, in spite of the snow. He feels better in this isolation, and in the concen‑ tration on his studies, his health has improved and will go on improving in a state which from month to month grows more calm. How unhappy I am not to be any longer my own master so that I could fly this instant to your side. I am proud enough to believe that my presence would give you some relief. I shall certainly make the journey this year but am unable to fix the date now. I cannot leave the king after an absence of nine months. I shall probably be free in May or June only to return about the first of July to accompany the king to Teplice, or after my return from Bohemia in August. But there is nothing more certain than that my plans will be guided by yours if I had the smallest hope that you would like to come to Germany, to see the observatories of Göttingen, Altona, Königsberg (Frauenhofer's great heliometer built for Bessel), if you would stay with me, dear friend, I should come to meet you at the German frontier if you came alone and if my company could help to diminish the boredom of hearing German spoken. I have only one wish in the world, to see you, to do what would be agreeable for you. I am equally resigned to the idea that you would not like to see the monotony of the countries in which I have my being; I shall come to you. But I think that you might find some consolation in the work which Mme. Arago, jealous for your reputation, liked to see you do: a *treatise on astronomy*, followed by a physical geography which none could do better; your *optics* . . . a short stay in Germany and the contact with some scientists of this country, Bessel, Struve, Gauss, Liebig, Mitscherlich, would perhaps revive some of the ideas which have been in your mind too long without being communicated to the world.

I do not quite know if in this first letter after my return to Europe, I may dare to speak to you of science and my feeble efforts; I shall finish this winter my journey of the Andes and at the same time my *physics of the universe*, the latter in German. In the spring when the observations have been calculated and when Rose has made the analyses indispensable for certain geognostic views, I shall publish a small volume in French, *Journey made at the order of the Emperor of All Russia to the mountains of the Ural and Altay, to the border of Chinese Dzungaria and the Caspian Sea,*

containing nothing but geological, magnetic and astronomical observations. My health has gained by the journey which has left me great
memories of the varied aspect of the Asiatic people. I implore you to
write me a few words of friendship.[5]

In July of that year, the Bourbons, who had struggled very
hard to make inroads on the constitution forced upon them by
the French revolution, finally lost the confidence of the French
nation; they had to give up the throne and the House of Orléans
came to power. Liberal opinion in Berlin was jubilant in the
hope that the example of a constitutional monarchy in Paris,
which had been attained without any violent upheaval, might
calm down the fears of the Prussian king and aristocracy and at
last produce the longed-for constitution. Everybody watched
the new French government with hopeful expectations; even
Gauss, who was not a particularly progressive man where
politics were concerned, expressed his optimism to Humboldt.
He knew his French, however, and his reply was rather damp-
ing: 'Believe me, my wishes agree with yours but my hopes are
rather feeble. For forty years, I have seen governments change in
Paris; they always fall through their own incompetence; new
promises take the place of the old but are not fulfilled, and the
same pernicious course begins again. I have known and sometimes trusted most of the men of the moment; there were excellent and well-meaning people among them but they could not
keep up the pace. Soon, they were no better than their predecessors and often even bigger scoundrels. So far, no government has kept its word with the people, none has subordinated
its selfishness to the common weal. As long as that does not
happen, no government will have permanency in France. The
nation has been defrauded every time and will be defrauded
again. And then it will again punish the fraud and deception,
for it is strong and mature enough for that.'[6]

The Prussian government hesitated at first to recognize the
new régime but the absence of any revolutionary symptoms in
France provided sufficient encouragement for the king to send

Humboldt to Paris with the royal letter of recognition; and at the beginning of October, the two friends were reunited. Arago had been elected permanent secretary of the *Institut* in June, after the death of Fourier. It is no exaggeration to say that from now until the death of Arago in 1853, Humboldt exerted a decisive influence on the choice of new foreign correspondents and associates, his advice caused his contemporaries a good deal of resentment but the hindview of posterity can only confirm his unhesitating predilection for the best minds of his time.

Eleven

CENTRAL ASIAN GEOGRAPHY

WHILE Arago, who had been driven into politics by his pronounced liberal opinions, attended the meetings of the Chamber of Deputies, Humboldt began work on the results of his Asiatic journey. It was left to Rose to publish an account of the itinerary and the mineralogical and geological observations, an account which is as long as it is tedious. Humboldt's work, *Asie Centrale*, did not appear until 1843. The first two volumes contain an exposition of the structure and extent of the moun/tain ranges and plateaux. The description was not restricted to the regions covered by the expedition but included all the in/formation about the largely unknown ranges of the Himalayas, Tien/shan and Kunlun which Humboldt had been able to collect from Russian sources in contact with Asiatic merchants in Siberia, and a good deal of conjecture as well. It does not seem to the uninitiated that geography is a discipline amenable to theorizing, but a good deal of geographical reputation was made in the eighteenth and early nineteenth century by men who had never left their native country. The determination of latitudes and longitudes, made by Humboldt, were incor/porated in a map, and the measurements tabulated. In addition, there is a section on the history of the geography of Asia which includes an account of Chinese geography and the use of the magnetic compass in ancient China, contributed by the Sino/logists Julien and Klaproth on Humboldt's request. In the third volume, the climatological and magnetic observations made by Humboldt on the whole journey are collected and analysed. The work was dedicated to the Emperor of Russia: 'It is my pleasant and sacred duty to lay down here the tribute of my vivid and respectful gratitude', a statement which Humboldt confessed to have found difficult to make.

The main importance of *Asie Centrale* lies in the exposition of Humboldt's ideas on the relative contribution of mountains and plateaux to the mean height of continents. The strong visual impression of mountain ranges had led observers to overestimate their contribution to the mean elevation of the region above sea level. Humboldt, who believed in the necessity for substantiating scientific statements with figures, tried to calculate the mean heights which would be attained if the rocks forming mountain ranges were uniformly spread over the continents. In this computation, the inhomogeneity of the constituents of the soil must be left out of consideration, and the shape of mountain ranges was approximated by that of a triangular prism. The results which Humboldt obtained were surprising; they proved the relative unimportance of the highest mountain ranges compared with extended plateaux. He found the mean height above sea level of the North American area to be 749 feet; for South America, the figure is 1,133 feet, for Asia 1,152 and for Europe 672 feet; no observations were at that time available for the continents of Africa and Australia. Nothing was known either about Tibet proper or Chinese Tartary, as Humboldt called it; from scattered data on localities just east of Kailas, he estimated the mean height of the whole district to be 11,500 feet. Laplace had introduced the concept of the mean height of the continents in his *Mécanique Celeste* which was published in 1825; he had needed some such smoothing out of the surface features of the earth for his investigation into the reasons for the flattening at the poles. 'The agreement shown by the pendulum experiments with the flattening obtained by the measurements of terrestrial degrees and the lunar inequalities, prove that the surface of the terrestrial spheroid would be nearly that of the equilibrium state if that surface were fluid. From that and from the fact that the sea leaves vast continents uncovered, it can be concluded that it must have little depth, and that its mean depth is of the same order as the mean height of the continents and islands above sea level, a height which does not exceed 3,280 feet. This height is thus a small fraction of the excess of the equatorial over the polar radius, an excess which surpasses 12·4 miles. Just as high mountains cover some parts of the continents, so there will be large cavities in the basin of the oceans; but it is natural to think that their depth is smaller than the height of high mountains since the silt of the rivers and the remains of marine animals, carried along by the currents, will gradually fill up these great cavities.'[1]

Humboldt's calculations had given a figure of 927 feet for the mean height of the then known world, a figure much below Laplace's estimate. It was also known at the time that the mean depth of the oceans surpasses the mean height of the continents. Worried by the disagreement between the numerical data and Laplace's ideas, Humboldt consulted Poisson who gave the following interpretation: 'M. Laplace says that the depth of the sea must be small compared with the excess of the major over the minor radius of the earth, an excess which is approximately twelve miles. The data on which he bases his assumptions, are not sufficient to fix the precise limits of the relationship between this depth and the excess; it could be one-twentieth and the depth about 1,700 feet, etc., I do not believe that that would be contrary to the theory. The author also says that the mean depth is of the same order as the mean height of the continents which does not surpass 3,000 feet. The word "order" leaves a great deal of latitude; it means only that the ratio of the depth to the difference between the two radii is not large compared to the ratio of the height to the same difference, that for example the first ratio is not ten or fifteen times greater than the second. I believe that the expressions used by M. Laplace permit the admission that the first ratio may be two, three times, perhaps even four times greater than the second, provided always that the mean height of the continents and the mean depth of the oceans will both be very small compared with the excess of one radius over the other. If I have occasion in future to occupy myself with the theory of this question, I shall be very pleased to find myself provided with more precise data than those which served our illustrious friend.'[2] This reply does not dispose of Laplace's mistaken assumption that the deepest places in the oceans are less low than the height of the highest mountains; it is now well established that they far surpass them just as the plains at the bottom of the sea surpass the continental plains in evenness.

The history of the Caspian and Aral Sea and the river system of the Amu-darya and Syr-darya, the Oxus and Jaxartes of the Greeks, is discussed in great detail. All the historical sources have been examined, ranging from Herodotus to the early Chinese geographers and medieval Arabs, from Marco Polo to the Merchant Adventurers of Elizabethan times and from the memoirs of a Tartar prince of the seventeenth century to the publications of Sir Alexander Burnes. Humboldt was convinced that there was formerly a connection between the Caspian and Lake Aral south of the plateau of Ust-Urt; at that time the two inland seas formed one vast basin. It became gradually marshy, and the connecting basin finally dried out completely in the excessively arid climate of Inner Asia. His historical studies made it quite certain that the Oxus flowed originally into the Caspian before that arm dried out through accumulated silt when the present course of the river became established. In our time, the Turkmen canal has opened the connection between the two inland seas again although it does not follow the old river bed in detail. A similar example of such shifting river beds is given by the system of the Tarim in Sinkiang which altered its course about forty years ago moving back into a more northerly bed which, according to archaeological finds, must have existed once before, about sixteen hundred years ago.

The first observations of the level of the Caspian Sea were

made in Astrakhan by Lerche during the years 1732 to 1749; he found the height to be 326 feet below sea level, a result which was received with derision. Inokhodzov found the height of a small town in the district of Saratov as 182 feet below sea level in observations extending from 1770 to 1774. Savich and Sabler had reduced this value to 81 feet in 1837 and modern maps give 92 feet for the northern Caspian Sea.

The map of Central Asia given by Humboldt is now only a matter of curiosity. He based his sketch of the mountain ranges on the few data available and the information collected from the leaders of caravans together with partly misunderstood knowledge obtained from Chinese maps and writings. The Tien-shan appears in approximately the right position but the Kunlun keeps too much to a parallel of latitude. The Kara-koram range has moved too far north, and there are two parallel ranges, named Hindukho, while the name Hindukush is given to a peak. The most astounding piece of misunderstanding, however, is a range by the name of Bolor, the Chinese Tsung-ling, which runs north–south, intersecting the east–west ranges practically at a right angle. It is roughly parallel to the 72nd degree of longitude. In extent, it covers the region where the Himalaya, Kunlun and Tien-Shan meet the Hindukush and Pamir mountains. The mainly Chinese sources which Hum-boldt adduces in evidence, contain nothing about the direction of the ranges which had to be crossed from Ferghana into Kash-mir; on the other hand, this purely fictitious range of Bolor looks suspiciously like the southern part of the range called Immaus on Ptolemy's map of Asia. On Humboldt's map, the region of the desert Takla-Makan is marked as 'terra incognita', a challenge which inspired Sven Hedin to his explorations, which turned it into a well-mapped part of the world and gave rise to one of the most thrilling descriptions of determination and hardiness.

Humboldt's map of Central Asia contains two entirely fictitious volcanoes near the Tien-shan range, the Pe-shan north of Kucha and the Ho-cheu north-east of Turfan, which, he claims, have been active in historical times and which seem to be the result of a misunderstanding of Chinese sources. The position of the Ho-cheu is still marked on a map of Stanford's London Atlas, printed in 1904. Humboldt quotes as evidence for their existence the following two extracts from Chinese geographies of the eighteenth century as translated by Julien:

At a distance of 30 li (3 leagues) west of *Burgabulak* (a Dzungar word meaning the *well of poplars*, where poplars grow), which is a dependency of Urumtchi, there is a region whose circumference forms about 100 li (10 leagues); out of its middle, clouds of ashes rise constantly (literally flying ashes). If some object (combustible) is thrown into it, a flame is seen to rise, and in a few moments it is reduced to ashes. If a stone is thrown into it, black smoke is seen to rise suddenly which subsides only after a fairly long time.

In this country, the snow which falls in the winter, covers the soil to a height of ten feet; but in this place, no trace of it can be seen. It is called *Ho-hien*, i.e. a *pit of fire*. The birds dare not fly over it.[3]

This description may, of course, indicate the presence of oil; Humboldt always included the occurrence of oil and natural gas among the volcanic phenomena.

The second passage reads:

Between Urumtchi and Ili, there is a circular terrain of 90 li (9 leagues). Seen from afar, it appears white as snow. The terrain seems impregnated with salt. After rain, it becomes hard and solid. If a large stone is thrown down there, a noise is heard as if an iron plate were struck with a piece of wood. If a man or an animal inadvertently sets foot on this terrain, he sinks into the ground after a few steps as if he had fallen into a ditch, and disappears for ever. This place is commonly called Hoei-hien, i.e. the *pit of ashes*.[4]

These two descriptions, which do not seem to apply to the same phenomenon at all, are supposed to refer to the volcano Pe-shan or white mountain near Kucha. The volcano Ho-cheu is placed between Turfan and Pidjan which is nowadays called Shan-shan on Chinese maps, at the entrance of a desert notorious for its north-westerly gales. Humboldt quotes the following passage in support of its existence:

In the summer, the heat is excessive. A belt of sand hills stretches from the east towards the south where no plants, no trees are to be seen. The mountains give off more dazzling flashes than the sun. In the winter, there is neither strong frost nor snow. They are commonly called Ho-yen-shan, i.e. the mountains of the fiery pits. This country produces wheat, flax, melons, grapes, in short numerous fruit of an excellent quality.[4]

Again, there is that curious confusion between white mountains, here even called sandy, and fiery eruptions. Humboldt tentatively ascribed the dazzling colour to the reflection of pumice stone. Another and non-volcanic interpretation is suggested by the discovery by Sven Hedin and Sir Aurel Stein of the abandoned settlement of Lou-lan to the east of the present-day Lopnor in the basin of the river Tarim. In the first three centuries of our era, the Tarim had a more northern course, ending in a salt marsh called Pu-chang at that time. To the north-east, the old road to Tun-huang, the first outpost of China, passed through the White Dragon Mounds which are described by Shui-king, the author of the *Book of Rivers*, in the following words: 'This region has an extent of 1,000 li; it consists entirely of salt, but of salt in a dry, solid state. There, the travellers spread pieces of felt for their animals to lie on. If the soil is dug up, blocks of salt are found as big as large pillows and piled up in a regular manner. In this district, the air is hazy like rising mist or like fluttering clouds; the sun and the stars are seldom seen there. Few live animals are seen, but many demons and dragons.'[5]

Lou-lan flourished west of the salt marsh, and farther south, an oasis Shan-shan existed until the seventh century. They were deserted when the Tarim shifted its course to the south and the Takla-Makan claimed its own again, and their existence was completely forgotten. The memory of Shan-shan persisted for a while until the new name Lopnor came into use for the terminal lake of the southern course of the Tarim which has now been abandoned again. Marco Polo mentions the resting place of Lop in his account and tells stories of the wicked demons of the desert; but the salt marsh in the north remained unknown to him.

In the succeeding centuries, the rule of the Mongols in Central Asia cut China off from all knowledge of East Turki-stan. When it became again a Chinese possession in the eighteenth century, they did not find it easy to identify the localities with the names given in the descriptions of their classical writers. In the new maps, Lou-lan and Shan-shan were at first left indiscriminately in the south of Lopnor. Later, both names were placed to the north of the lake but much too far north, in the region between Turfan and Hami, where a small place with the local name of Pidjan still bears the official Chinese designation Shan-shan. Humboldt's volcano Ho-cheu is marked in exactly that position while the descriptions of the eighteenth-century Chinese sources have a marked resemblance to that of the White Dragon Mounds.

During Humboldt's Russian journey, the first diamonds were found in the Urals; his travelling companion Rose has traced the history of the find in his account. The stones were discovered on the gold placer deposit of Count Polier, a Frenchman who had married a Russian woman, the owner of a number of profitable mines in the Urals.

At Kushvinsk, our charming travelling companion, Count Polier, left us and travelled to his possessions on the western slope of the Ural. The journey of Count Polier resulted in an event of great importance for the mineralogy of the Ural, the discovery of Russian diamonds. The find of this precious mineral, so long supposed to be confined to the tropics, has excited so much interest that we want to discuss the fact in some detail; it seems necessary and appropriate since historically inaccurate paragraphs have been published by some newspapers, and since the discoverers, Mr. Schmidt and Count Polier have been companions of our expedition since our embarkation at Gorkiy.

In his geognostic work on the stratification of rocks in the two hemispheres, Mr. Humboldt had drawn attention to the curious analogy of the simultaneous occurrence of minerals which characterise in different localities the beds of platinum and gold sands. For instance, in Brazil at Corrego das Lagens there occur gold, platinum, palladium and diamonds, near Tejuco gold and diamonds, on the Rio Abaete platinum and diamonds. These ideas of the association of minerals had awakened in him and, as he says expressly in his *Fragmens asiatiques*, much earlier (1826) in our friend, Professor Engelhardt of Tartu and in Mr. Mamyshev, the former director of the Goroblagodatsk mine, the greatest hope that diamonds might be found in the Urals. In consequence we directed our attention in particular to the occurrence of diamonds whenever we came to a gold mine and examined the gold-bearing sand under the microscope in order to discover the minerals accompanying gold and platinum from which to find out the original gold deposit. We separated only the lighter, dust-like particles from the sand so that the coarser residue could be more easily examined; if the concentration is driven too far, the lighter, non-metallic substances are washed away with the quartz and only magnetite and chromatite are left behind with the gold and platinum. In these continuous microscopic investigations we succeeded in finding crystals which had hitherto been unknown in the gold sands of the Urals, and which kept us in constant expectation since they occur in Brazil in the company of diamonds. Thus we discovered at the very first placer deposit which we visited, and later nearly everywhere, small zircons which by their diamond-like sparkle often deceived us. But our eager search for diamonds met with no success; and not until the 3rd of September did we hear the news that our companions, Mr. Schmidt and Count Polier had made the noteworthy discovery on the 5th of July, only four days after our separation from them, on the western slopes of the mountain range. Count Polier made Mr. Humboldt a present of one of the stones with the request not to announce the discovery at our return to St. Petersburg since the Russian gems had not yet been presented to the sovereign of the country.[6]

Polier sent a long report to Cancrin on the remarkable discovery: 'On the 5th of July, I arrived with Mr. Schmidt, the young mineralogist from Freyberg, in the gold placer work; and on the same day, the first diamond of the Urals was dis﹣ covered in the gold sand put before me, between a quantity of pyrite and quartz. It had been found the day before by a fourteen﹣year﹣old boy, Pavel Popov from the village of Kalin﹣ skoye. This boy was employed at the establishment and had hastened to give his find to the foreman since a reward had been announced for anybody who found unusual stones. The foreman, however, had not thought such a small stone of any importance and had put it with the other minerals which he handed over to me. Its transparency was perfect, and that alone together with its lustre would have proved to us that it was a diamond even if the crystallization with rounded surfaces could have left any doubts that Humboldt's prophecy had come true. Three days afterwards, another boy found a second stone, and a few days after my departure, a third was sent to me which was bigger than the first two together.'[7]

The Times reported the discovery on the 14th of July 1830 together with a history of the events leading to it; all honour is due to Pavel Popov who had the wits to recognize that he had found something unusual. In the following years, a few more stones came to light, and by the end of the century, 220 diamonds from the Urals were known to exist. But over a hundred years had to pass before Humboldt's optimistic prophecy that 'the true pocket, the rich nest' would be un﹣ covered, was fulfilled. The real deposits were discovered in 1948 and 1954 in the basin of Nishneya Tunguska and a kimberlite pipe in the basin of Daldyn in north﹣west Yakutia, near the Arctic circle.

The third volume of Humboldt's book on Central Asia is concerned with comparative climatology, in particular with the causes for the deviation of the isothermal lines from the geographical circles of latitude. If the climate of any locality were entirely determined by the amount of heat it receives from the sun, the isothermal lines should be circles parallel to the equator. Humboldt's early maps of the isothermal lines had already shown that even in the tropics they deviate greatly from the lines of equal geographical latitude. His journey through Russia into Siberia gave him the opportunity to investigate the climatology of a great northern land mass.

The configuration of Central Asia and the great *depression* of the north-western part (the Kapchak, the Khorezm, the basins of the Caspian and Aral Seas, the Turan of the orient) exercise a profound influence on the climate and the succession of meteorological phenomena. The geo-logical picture of a continent is in consequence intimately connected with climatology and the geography of plants.

It is known in our present state of information that the shape of the continents, the structure of the soil in its horizontal extent as well as the inequality of the curvature of the surface, the relative position of opaque masses (continental) and the transparent and liquid masses (oceanic), the direction of the great mountain systems and the preponderance of certain winds, which is determined by the caloric (absorbing and emitting) powers of the envelope of the globe, all these are the most general causes of the climatic differences. Only large-scale geographical aspects can be the guide in research into the temperatures of Asia. As we move on the same parallel from western Europe towards the east, the rigours of winter are seen to increase rapidly; this phenomenon has for a long time been assumed to be due to a progressive elevation of the soil in vast plateaux; to a single refrigerating cause and a cause which has wrongly been sup-posed to exist over an immense area, has been ascribed a phenomenon which is produced by several causes all at the same time, in particular by the uniform enlargement of the ancient continent towards the east, by the distance from the coast, i.e. from an oceanic basin, a heat reservoir of little variation in the west, by the western winds which are land winds in eastern Europe and the whole of Asia and which predominate north of the tropics. Accurate barometric measurements have entirely changed our ideas of the elevation of the soil in this part of the world. . . . The small elevation of the continental masses in eastern Europe deserves atten-tion if the phenomenon is considered from the point of view of the average relief of the continent leaving apart the partial and more recent phenom-enon of the mountain ranges and the local intumescences sometimes pre-sented by the ground of the plains in the neighbourhood of the ranges.

From the heaths of northern Brabant one can travel, even over the passes of the Urals, to the Asiatic steppes which surround the western slope of the Altay, and to Chinese Dzungaria without crossing a height of 1,300 or 1,400 feet. At high latitudes, beyond 60° to 65°, continuous plains will be found over a distance nearly equal to half the circumference of the world.

Thus it is not the elevation of the ground which causes the concave inflexion of the isothermal lines along a parallel of latitude from the central parts of Europe towards the east.

The position of different mountain systems (either in continuous chains or in isolated or sporadic groups) and the relation between these systems and the more or less elevated plains have a great influence on the distribution of temperatures and their irregularity caused by atmospheric currents.

The fundamental basis of climatology is thus a precise knowledge of the unevenness of the surface of a continent. Without this *hypsometric* knowledge, the inflexion of the isothermal lines is attributed to the elevation of the ground when it is the effect of different causes in lowlying regions. In penetrating from northeastern Europe into Asia, a decrease of the mean annual temperature is observed together with a more unequal distribution of this temperature between the seasons, a distribution caused by the continental structure of Asia (structure of large land masses with few sinuosities) and by the position of this continent with respect to the equator, the polar ice and the influence of the western winds. Under the influence of the above mentioned circumstances, Europe and Asia offer the following contrasts.

Europe with a sinuous configuration, interrupted by bays and arms of the sea, so to speak *articulated*, forms the western part of the old continent: it is only a *peninsular continuation* of *Asia*, just as Brittany with its mild winters and cool summers is a peninsular continuation of the rest of France. Europe receives predominantly western winds which, for the western and central parts, are sea winds, currents which have been in contact with a mass of water whose surface temperature even in the month of January does not fall below 48° to 51° (in the latitudes of 45° to 50°). Europe enjoys the beneficial influence of a large terrestrial, tropical zone (that of Africa and Arabia) between the meridians of Lisbon and Kazan which, by absorption of the solar radiation, becomes much hotter at the surface than an oceanic tropical zone, and which, as a result of the ascending currents, pours masses of warm air on countries approaching closely to the north pole. Europe, considered as the western *peninsular continuation* of Asia, has other advantages which, until now, have not found sufficient appreciation. Such are the lesser and unequal development of the continent towards the north, the oblique shape, the direction from the southwest towards the northeast. The continental part of Europe, over the first third of its western length, does not extend beyond the 52nd degree of latitude. A second, more central third, enlarged by Scandinavia, is crossed by the Arctic circle. In the most easterly third, east of the meridian of St Petersburg where the spreading continent shows the character of an asiatic climate, the Arctic circle no more than grazes the northern coast; but this coast is bathed by a zone of the Arctic Ocean whose winter temperature is very different from that of the same sea west of the North Cape. The direction of the great *oceanic valley* which separates Europe from America, and the existence of that river of warm water (*gulf stream*) which flows at first from SSW to NNE and then from west to east and skirts the coast of Norway, have a powerful influence on the limits of the polar ice, on the contours of this belt of frozen solid water which opens a vast gulf to the liquid waters between eastern Greenland, Spitsbergen and the northern extremity of the Scandinavian peninsula. Europe has the advantage to be opposite to this gulf and consequently separated from the polar ice by an open sea. In the winter, this belt advances to the 75th degree of latitude between Novaya Zemlya, the mouth of the Lena and the archipelago of New Siberia; in the summer, it withdraws at the meridian of the North Cape and more towards the west, between Spitsbergen and eastern Greenland to the 80th and 81st degree of latitude. Furthermore, the winter limit of the pack ice, i.e. the line along which the ice has its nearest approach to continental Europe, does not enclose Bear Island; and in the coldest season it is possible to navigate freely from the North Cape to the southern promontory of Spitsbergen, across a sea whose temperature is raised by currents from the southwest. The pack ice is diminished there, where it finds a free outlet to the polar region, as in Baffin Bay and between Iceland and Spitsbergen. Captain Sabine observed a mean temperature of 42° at the surface of the Atlantic Ocean between 65° and 70°; in the same latitudes, the European continent shows a mean annual temperature below freezing point. . . .

The Asian continent stretches beyond the 70th degree over an east–west line which is thirteen times longer than Europe; between the mouths of the Lena and the Yenisey, it reaches the 75th degree, i.e. the latitude of Bear Island. Its northern coasts touch everywhere the winter limit of the pack ice; the summer limit withdraws only in a few places and for a short time from the coast. The north winds, unchecked by any moun-tain ranges in the open plains, pass over a sheet of snow-covered ice. This sheet forms, so to speak, a continuation of the continent, on one side towards the north right up to the pole, on the other towards the north-east into the region of maximum cold which Sir David Brewster places at a longitude of 80° east of Greenwich while Erman believes it to be near Cape Taimoura, 9° more towards the east. Only a small part of the Asian land mass is exposed to the action of the tropical sun. The equator passes over the ocean between the meridians which limit the eastern and western extremities (over an immense space of 121 degrees of longitude); with the exception of small parts of Sumatra, Borneo, Celebes and Halmahera, no land is placed under the equator. That part of Asia which lies in the temperate zone, is therefore less exposed to the effect of those ascending currents from which Europe benefits as a result of Africa's position.

If we confine ourselves to general considerations, to the large-scale characteristics of the Asiatic climate, we find further causes of the lower temperatures in the horizontal configuration, the shape of the contours, the unevenness of the surface in the vertical direction and its position east of the European continent. North of the 30th parallel, Asia displays an accumulation of continuous land masses, without bays or notable peninsular extensions. Great mountain systems, aligned in an east–west direction and whose highest ranges border on the subtropical regions, form an extended barrier against the south winds. High-lying plateaux are found between the mountain clusters of Kashmir and Ladakh and the sources of the Orkhon, in a direction SW–NE; they pass through low-lying regions or form their boundary; they hold the snow until the middle of the summer and lower the temperature in neighbouring countries by the action of descending currents. These plateaux vary and *individualise* the climates east of the sources of the Oxus, of the Ala-Tau and the Tarbagatay, in the depth of Central Asia, between the parallels of the Himalaya and the Altay. Finally, the whole length of Europe separates Asia from a sea to the west of the western coast which, in the temperate zone, is always warmer than the eastern coast of a continent, provided that the mean temperature is not diminished by a cold oceanic current. The enormous broadening of Europe in the direction of the meridians which begins at the gulf of Finland, contributes to the refrigera, ting action of the predominantly western winds which become land winds for that part of the ancient world which is placed to the east of the wall of the Urals.

The contrasts between Europe and Asia which I have summarily indicated, represent the group of causes which affect the inflexions of the lines of equal annual temperatures and the unequal distribution of this mean value between the different seasons, phenomena which become particularly noticeable east of the meridian of St. Petersburg, there where the continent of Europe connects up with northern Asia. The east of Europe and the whole of Asia north of the 35th degree of latitude have pre-eminently a continental climate, if this expression is used as opposed to that of the climate of islands and western coasts, according to the definitions given by Mr. Leopold von Buch. As a result of their shape and position with respect to the west and south-west winds, they have an excessive climate, analogous to that of the United States, i.e. very warm summers are succeeded by extremely severe winters. Nowhere in the world, not even in Italy or the Canaries, have I seen better grapes than at Astrakhan near the shore of the Caspian Sea (mean annual tempera, ture only $50 \cdot 4°$); and yet in the same locality and more to the south at the mouth of the river Terek (in the latitude of Avignon and Rimini), the thermometer often descends in the winter to $45-54°$ below freezing point.[8]

His experience of the *excessive* climate of Russia, to use Buffon's expression, showed Humboldt that the mean annual temperature does not suffice to characterize the climate of a country; his tables now contained the mean temperatures for the four seasons as well, and the new maps divided the iso- thermal lines into isochimenals or lines of equal winter tem- peratures and isotherals or lines of equal summer tempera- tures. As he saw, it is the rise of the thermometer from winter to summer which is the truly representative quantity, and he tried even to calculate the rise or gradient in temperature per month for the varying climates, but it does not seem to have occurred to him to draw maps of the gradients or differential coefficients, proof that he was not a mathematician, as he had been told by his contemporaries, a reproof at which he had often taken umbrage.

A striking feature of the Siberian climate is the low tempera￾ture of the soil even at the height of the summer when the ther￾mometer rises to 87° in the open air. At latitudes corresponding to those of Scotland, the ground was found to be frozen at a depth of six feet under the surface, and the congealed soil, mixed with ice crystals, might reach a thickness of ten feet. Other travellers had observed that this underground ice was a general feature of Siberian geography. Humboldt saw in this condition of the ground the explanation for the state of pre￾servation in which mastodons had been found on the slopes of the Urals and in northern Siberia, and considered that it was not necessary to evoke the postulate of the existence of a glacial period to account for the occurrence of elephants in a re￾markable state of preservation so far north, since he himself had had evidence of the occasional appearance of tigers in southern Siberia. An earthquake or any other sudden change of the sur￾face of the soil might easily have been responsible for the destruc￾tion of the animals, and the low temperature of the ground would have prevented complete decomposition of the bodies. Humboldt felt initially very sceptical at the idea of former glacial epochs which was first propounded in 1837 by the Swiss scientist Louis Agassiz, who was then only thirty years old but already well known as an authority on fossil fish. In particular, he objected to a sudden change in the climate of the earth such as had been postulated by Agassiz in his *Étude sur les glaciers*: 'The surface of Europe adorned before by a tropical vegetation and inhabited by troops of large elephants, enormous hippopotami and gigantic carnivora, was suddenly buried under a vast mantle of ice, covering alike plains, lakes, seas and plateaux.'[9] To Humboldt who saw the history of the earth as a steady cooling of the outer crust from its originally liquid state, and who had observed the remarkable constancy of the mean temperatures, the hypothesis of one or more glacial periods appeared as sheer apostasy. He wrote to Agassiz in 1837: 'With reference to the general or periodical lowering of the temperature of the globe, I have never thought it necessary, on account of the elephant of the Lena, to admit the sudden frost of which Cuvier used to speak. What I have seen in Siberia, and what has been observed in Captain Beechey's expedition on the north-west coast of America, simply proves that there exists a layer of frozen drift, in the fissures of which (even now) the muscular flesh of any animal which should accidentally fall into them, would be preserved intact. It is a slight local phenomenon. To me, the ensemble of geological phenomena seems to prove, not the prevalence of this glacial surface on which you would carry along your boulders, but a very high temperature spreading almost to the poles, a tempera-ture favourable to organizations resembling those now living in the tropics. Your ice frightens me.'[10]

Three years later, he tried to be more conciliatory about this new idea: 'I cannot close this letter without asking your pardon for some expressions, too sharp perhaps, in my former letters, about your vast geological conceptions. The very exaggeration of my expressions must have shown you how little weight I attached to my objections. . . . My desire is always to listen and to learn. Taught from my youth to believe that the organisa-tion of past times was somewhat tropical in character, and startled therefore at these glacial interruptions, I cried "Heresy" at first. But should we not always listen to a friendly voice like yours? I am interested in whatever is printed on these topics; so, if you have published anything at all on the ensemble of your geological ideas, have the great kindness to send it to me through a bookseller.'[11]

However, only a few months later, he repeated his early objections again to Sir Roderick Murchison: 'You know how highly I think of Agassiz, how much I recognise his immense services to geology. I also like the courageous independence with which he defends what he considers true and important. Science can only gain by this freedom. I believe that there were formerly glaciers where there are none now but so far I cannot admit that erratic blocks have come to us with and on the ice; I consider it unnecessary to postulate ice caps which covered the whole world, paroxysms of alternating heat and cold which periodically extinguished animal life. These convulsions frighten me.'[12]

Nearly forty years earlier, Humboldt's idea of a volcanic age had been just as displeasing to Goethe, a strict adherent to the idea of a peaceful and gradual evolution.

His work on Central Asia, in contrast to his American books, did not touch at all on political and economic matters, as he had promised to Cancrin. He had kept to his intentions, outlined in a letter written in 1831: 'I shall never write memoranda on the organisation and administration of the mines; I shall only treat of physical and geognostic subjects. I shall never write an account of the journey; to avoid the reefs of both reproof and flattery and since it is not my duty to make difficulties for myself, I shall only print observations of an inanimate nature and many figures which are the most innocent hieroglyphs of thought.'[13]

Twelve

ORGANIZATION OF INTERNATIONAL SCIENTIFIC COLLABORATION

HUMBOLDT was now over sixty years old; the era of expeditions into the unknown was over. Until a few years before his death, however, he travelled about Europe, to the Czech spas with the king and to Paris and Arago whenever he could obtain leave of absence from the court or was sent there on a political mission. In his youth, he had made his journeys on foot or horseback and in sailing boats; with the same equanimity, he now used steamers and trains. He was as restlessly active in the continuation of his magnetic observations and in following the development of all branches of science. His creativeness had left him but not his enthusiasm. Even when he was well over eighty, people noticed, with surprise and a slight shock at this lack of decorum, that his eyes sparkled like those of a young man when he talked about science. His enormous knowledge and his unfailing interest in the efforts of other scientists made him more and more the grand old man of science; his extraordinarily large correspondence kept him in contact with new discoveries, but also exposed him to an inordinate number of begging letters of a refined type, petitions to the king or the ministers for support in some scientific or technical project. To reply to all these letters went beyond his strength; he did not know where to begin; but all the cases which were not merely pretentious or downright cranky were put before the authorities and their progress ensured with a pertinacity which sometimes extended over years, even if success came when it was too late; it so happened that the mathematicians Abel and Eisenstein died, both of tuberculosis, just when Humboldt had secured financial help for them. He was as generous with his time in the pursuit of official recognition for unrecognized merit as he was generous with unofficial assistance for his protégés from his own pocket, so that the palaeontologist and geologist Agassiz, who had had some experience of it, could say that towards the end of Humboldt's life, there was hardly a prominent scientist in the world who was not under some obligation to him.

The young Agassiz had arrived in Paris in the spring of 1832 with very little money and no resources; his father was an impecunious clergyman in the canton of Neufchâtel in Switzerland, at that time actually a Prussian enclave. He had come to search through the collections of the Natural History Museum for his book on fossil fish; out of eight pounds monthly he had to pay an artist for the necessary illustrations. Humboldt, to whom he had had an introduction, took great interest in the promising young man and was much perturbed when Agassiz confessed that he was on the verge of giving up his scientific work. When his attempt to interest the German publisher Cotta in Agassiz's book met with no response, he came to the rescue himself. 'I am very uneasy, my dear M. Agassiz, at being still without any letter from Cotta. Has he been prevented from writing by business, or illness perhaps? You know how tardy he always is about writing. Yesterday (Monday) I wrote to him earnestly again concerning your affair (an undertaking of such moment for science), and urged upon him the issuing of the fossil and fresh-water fishes in alternate numbers. In the meantime, I fear that the protracted delay may weigh heavily on you and your friends. A man so laborious, so gifted, and so deserving of affection as you are should not be left in a position where lack of serenity disturbs his power of work. You will then surely forgive my friendly goodwill toward you, my dear M. Agassiz, if I entreat you to make use of the accompanying small credit. You would do more for me

I am sure. Consider it an advance which need not be paid for years, and which I will gladly increase when I go away, or even earlier. It would pain me deeply should the urgency of my request made in the closest confidence,—in short, a transaction as between two friends of unequal age,—be disagreeable to you. I should wish to be pleasantly remembered by a young man of your character.'[1] The small credit was a draft for £40, about twothirds of Humboldt's monthly income; no wonder it never lasted beyond the tenth of the month. His overdraft was a continuous burden on his conscience, although—or rather because—his bankers, Mendelssohns, with an equal generosity never pressed him. To ensure that his rent would not rise any further, they even bought the house he lived in from his landlord. Humboldt's aversion to acquisitiveness went so far that he returned to his publisher part of the fee sent to him for some articles because he considered it excessive. 'I have written two essays for Cotta (not yet published) which are very much admired by his readers, a description of the plateau of Bogotá and on the fluctuation of gold since the middle ages. He sends me (four printed sheets) a draft for forty shilling, ten shilling the sheet. I feel inclined (much as I need money) to return half of it—but it just occurs to me while I am writing to Cotta, to find out what the maximum pay is nowadays for articles in a periodical, whether five, six or eight shilling are the rule. In that case, I shall return less.' Of a truly disinterested kindness, he expected no subservience in return. His attitude towards Agassiz remained quite unaffected by his dislike of the theory of glacial periods, and to Boussingault he wrote: 'The more you move away one day from my present ideas, the more I shall conclude, my dear Boussingault, that you have sought information from nature herself and observed with your own eyes. Do not be influenced by my stratification; call "above" what I call "below". That is the true way of discovering the truth.'[3] They were equals in the service of a common cause.

During his frequent stays in Paris, Humboldt returned to the existence of his younger days. He lived in lodgings or small hotels on the left bank in remote and inaccessible streets where only the more persistent of those with introductions and appeals would pursue him, and left early in the morning before the enemy got up and attacked. An impenetrable cubby-hole near the rooms of Arago at the *Institut* hid him during the day; at seven o'clock at night, he emerged to go out to dinner and to make his invariable round of visits. The hours he spent with Arago were more than ever the very core of his existence. When he was separated from him, he waited for his letters like a young girl. Arago was a very bad correspondent; he some-times let more than a year go by and Humboldt became more and more imploring: only five lines, just three lines, only to see his handwriting was quite enough. Even his valet Seifert watched the post anxiously and the arrival of the long-awaited note was for him a moment of personal triumph.

In the spring of 1835, Wilhelm Humboldt died. He had been suffering since the death of his wife from an uncontrollable trembling of the arms and legs, probably Parkinson's disease, and was finally carried away by pneumonia. Alexander was continually at his bedside during the last days of his brother's life; nevertheless, the press saw fit to announce that Wilhelm had been deserted by his family at the end. The society of Berlin, envious of the reputation of the upstart 'Prussian Dio-scuri', was nothing loath to be shown the clay feet of these intellectual wonders. A few hours before, Humboldt had written to a friend: 'I did not know that my old eyes could still cry so much', and to Arago: 'I have had the misfortune to lose my brother the night before yesterday. I am profoundly dejected. In great pains we think of those who are nearest to us; I feel a little easier in writing to you. . . . I am left very much alone. I hope I shall have the good fortune to be with you this year.'[4]

There were few men of his own generation left in Berlin

with whom he shared not so much interests as opinions and a scale of values. His position with the king was envied and resented; the life at court did not rise to a very high intellectual level. The princes were given to a crude boisterousness, and the old king never overcame his inarticulateness. A shy and gruff man, he did not even speak in complete sentences when he opened his mouth. The only closer friends of this later period of Humboldt's life were the surviving members of the Mendelssohn family, the banker Beer and his wife who were the parents of the composer Meyerbeer, and Varnhagen von Ense, Rachel Levin's husband, who held a higher post in the Ministry for Foreign Affairs and had made a name for himself as a historian of recent Prussian history. Intelligent and liberal-minded, he shared Humboldt's disgust for the reactionary politics of the time, a disgust which was sharpened by his lack of promotion. Several times he had been passed over for less able but better-born men. He was fourteen years younger than the celebrated Rachel whom he adored with an unwavering admiration for the penetration and fastidiousness of her mind. She had been nearly forty when they married; a great admirer of passionate love in other women's lives, she had not been really capable of very strong feelings herself but glowed in her husband's heroine worship. Her *salon*, which had once fascinated Thomas Young, flourished as before, the meeting-place of the political, artistic and intellectual stars of Berlin who were not too hidebound to like a heterogeneous gathering. Varnhagen's devotion to his wife was quite genuine in spite of the extravagance with which he expressed it. He liked to be in the know, and the diaries which he kept for the greater part of his professional life are an invaluable source for the historian; every political rumour, every development in the problems of the time, every spiteful bit of gossip have been set down for posterity.

The years between 1830 and 1845 were of the greatest importance for the history of geomagnetism and the development of international collaboration in the collection of geophysical data, in which Humboldt has played a hitherto unrealized leading rôle. In 1832, Gauss published his paper on the measurement of absolute magnetic intensities, in which the force between two magnets was expressed in terms of the known units of length, mass and time, millimetres, milligrams and seconds, doing away with the arbitrary measure of the intensity of the field which Humboldt had introduced in 1805. From now on, the magnetic force could be related to the absolute and standardized mechanical force, although the general use was slow in coming; as late as 1845 Humboldt's units were still preferred.

As soon as Humboldt received Gauss's publication, he sat down, translated it into French—the original was written in Latin—and sent it off the very next day to Arago who, as was his habit, did not immediately acknowledge its receipt. Humboldt, as was *his* habit, wrote again: 'I only ask your permission for the humble request to let me know through Mr. Valenciennes whether you have received a letter with a translation I made of the paper by Gauss on the magnetic intensity. . . . M. Gauss takes perhaps too great an interest in this work which has occupied him for eighteen months, and you would give me great pleasure, boring as my abstract may be, if the *Temps* (the Oracle of Meetings, read everywhere in Germany) could publish the good news that the *Institut* has been informed of the discovery which my friend, sensitive as any geometrician, believes to have made.'[5]

A year later, Gauss and Weber designed a new and much more sensitive magnetometer which was provided with Poggendorf's mirror suspension. The optical magnification produced by the fixed lamp and scale and the movable mirror brought the distance between scale and mirror down to one or two yards; in the old Prony telescope, about 400 yards were needed to observe the fluctuations of the magnetic declination. The use of an auxiliary magnet made it possible to determine the absolute intensity of the earth's field. It was now no longer necessary to approach the instrument for every reading, so that the perturbations through the formerly inevitable small draughts and temperature changes were eliminated. Gauss organized simultaneous observations in a number of observatories in Germany, Sweden and Italy, as well as in Dublin and Greenwich, which were all provided with his new instrument; from 1836 onwards, these stations, which formed the so-called Göttingen Association, synchronized their measurements in four yearly periods of twenty-four hours' duration. Readings were taken at five-minute intervals. Gauss would never admit that his interest in magnetism had been influenced in any way by Humboldt's investigations and his ideas on the necessity for a widespread international collaboration in the field.

So far the British Empire had not taken any larger part in this collaboration. In April 1836, Humboldt addressed a letter to the Duke of Sussex, whom he had known as a student in Göttingen and who was now President of the Royal Society, in which he tried to interest the Royal Society and the English Government in the establishment of magnetic observatories in the British possessions overseas, to complete the circle of magnetic records in the inhabited world. He proposed that permanent stations should be set up in Canada, St. Helena, at the Cape of Good Hope, in Jamaica, Ceylon and Australia. A committee was appointed by the Royal Society which warmly supported the scheme; in addition to the fixed observation posts, they recommended the government to equip a naval expedition for magnetic observations in the Antarctic seas.

Having fully laid before the Council the contents of M. de Humboldt's letter, we have now to offer an opinion upon the subject it embraces. There can, we consider, be no question of the importance of the plan of observation which is here proposed for the investigation of the phenomena of terrestrial magnetism, or of the prospect which such a plan holds out of the ultimate discovery of the laws by which such phenomena are governed. . . .

There are, however, other grounds on which such a proposition as that made by M. de Humboldt should be most cordially received by the Royal Society. This society is here called upon, as a member of a great confederation, to co-operate with several other members, already in active co-operation, for the attainment of an object which ought to be common to all, and to such a call the Royal Society can never be deaf. Those who know best what has been done by co-operation on a well-digested system, and what remains undone in many departments of science for the want of it, can best appreciate the benefits that would accrue to science, by the adoption of the extensive plan of co-operation advocated by M. de Humboldt. Independently of our acquiring a knowledge of the laws which govern the phenomena here proposed to be observed, we ought to look to the effect which the adoption of such a plan may have on other branches of science. The example being thus once set of extensive co-operation in a single department of science, we may anticipate that it would be eagerly adopted in others, where, although our knowledge may be in a much more advanced state than it is regarding the phenomena of terrestrial magnetism, still much remains to be accomplished, which can scarcely be effected by any other means. We might thus hope to see the united efforts of all the scientific societies in Europe directed to the prose-cution of inquiry in each department of science, according to the plan of co-operation best adapted for its development.[6]

Humboldt was particularly interested in world-wide, simul-taneous observations of the irregular and sudden changes in magnetic intensity and declination, the magnetic storms as they are now universally called. This expressive term was coined by Humboldt after his first observations of the phenomenon; it occurs for the first time in a letter published in Gilbert's *Annalen der Physik* of 21 December, 1806. The convulsive fluctuations of the magnet may have reminded him of the violent changes of the atmospheric electric charge which he had so often observed in the thunderstorms of tropical America. He continued using the expression in private letters and in his address to the Duke of Sussex; as the Royal Society report states, he ventures to say 'magnetic storms'. Humboldt had a great adroitness in coining new technical terms; in addition to the expressions already mentioned, the isotherms, isochimenes, isotherals, isogonics, isoclines and isodynamics, he was also the originator of the geological term 'Jura'. He used it tenta-tively at first when a visit to the Swiss and French Jura had convinced him that its limestone belonged to a geological formation of its own. As with 'magnetic storms', the word advanced from private use to become a generally accepted member of our scientific language.

In 1839, the British Government, urged by the Royal Society and the British Association under the leadership of Sir John Herschel, Sir Edward Sabine, Airy and Lloyd, decided to establish fixed stations in Canada and to equip an Antarctic expedition, which was put into the charge of Sir James Ross. His ships carried the necessary instruments for his own use as well as for the permanent observatories to be set up in Australia and New Zealand, St. Helena and the Cape of Good Hope. Provided with detailed instructions drawn up by the 'Com-mittee of Physics and Meteorology of the Royal Society relative to the observations to be made in the Antarctic expedition and in the magnetic observatories' and amplified by Humboldt in a letter to Lord Munro, the First Lord of the Admiralty, the men in charge of the operations, officers and non-commissioned officers of the Royal Artillery, faithfully adhered to the inter-nationally agreed schedule. Only once they failed, in Tasmania. To Humboldt's indignation, the Victorian Sunday inter-vened, and the twenty-four hour readings were not completed. 'Among the many simultaneous perturbations, observed in recent times, that of the 25th of September 1841 is one of the most memorable which was observed at Toronto in Canada, at the Cape of Good Hope, in Prague and partly in Tasmania. The English *Sunday celebration* which deems it sinful to read a scale after midnight on Saturday and to follow the entire development of the great natural phenomena of creation,

interrupted the observation of the magnetic storm which hap
pened on a Sunday in Tasmania in consequence of the differ
ence in longitude.'[7]

The indignation of the *Quarterly Review* was even greater.
'We are surprised that Baron Humboldt, usually so cautious in
imputing blame, should have thus attempted to cast ridicule
upon the English government and English men of science, and
upon such a ground. But the statement having been made in
ignorance of how these things are really managed with us, it
requires a word of explanation. It is quite certain that the
English philosophers declined to accede to the Göttingen
"terms", or fixed days of continued observation from five
minutes to five minutes for twenty-four hours or more, which
have been fixed, in defiance of the immemorial usage of all
Christian communities, UPON SUNDAYS, "for general
convenience" (of the Jews, we suppose). Here is no question of
whether the mode of keeping the Sabbath in Scotland or at
Geneva, in England, or at Rome, be most correct; it is no
question of whether amusements are to be indulged in or not;
whether or not the theatres should be shut; it is the simple
question whether the seventh day is to receive any distinctive
observance whatever—whether the hebdomadal division of
time, which even Laplace traced in its origin to the very dawn
of civilisation, is to be annihilated. Is there, we would ask, an
observatory in Europe which has not its *congés de Dimanche*? In
any country where we ever spent a Sunday it was claimed
even by those who wholly neglected its religious duties, by a
prescriptive and indefeasible right as a day of unbending, of
relaxation and of social converse. We need but mention a
single instance, because it expresses the extreme case of com
pliance with a usage handed down from the remotest genera
tions: we mean the practice of the Polytechnic School of Paris
where Sunday is kept "holiday". But our German friends
emancipated themselves even from these relics of an ancient
superstition, and declared that the first day of the week should

be the hardest day of all; when the whole energies, physical and intellectual, should be concentrated from minute to minute and from hour to hour (so long as the wants of nature could be postponed), on the incessant watching of three vibrating bars.' The justice of this last remark must have struck many a scientist in his more doubting moments. But it is by no means the end of the spirited defence of Sunday observance; out of a text of thirty-seven pages, three pages are devoted to the religious and humane reasons for stopping all work on Sunday. 'And where after all is the loss? Perhaps during the whole five years that the observations were intended to continue, a second great disturbance might not occur on Sunday, and in any period of observation six such will be observed for one that is missed.'[8]

The year 1838 was fateful for the theory of the geomagnetic field: Gauss published his mathematical treatment which made it possible to predict the values of the intensity, declination and inclination on any point of the earth, and to calculate the position of the magnetic poles from the known data. Humboldt tried hard, under Jacobi's tuition, to grasp the essentials of the mathematical method involved but they remained below his 'depressed horizon'. The magnetic south pole was located by Ross's measurements at $76°$ S and $154°$ E, in contradiction to Gauss's predicted values of $66°$ southern latitude and $146°$ eastern longitude; a recalculation proved that the discrepancy was due to a numerical error in the computations. This theory was an interpretation of the mean values of the three components of the geomagnetic field; the very small daily and secular variations do not enter into it. The final elucidation of the causes for the diurnal variations and the magnetic storms, which lie in the movements of electrical charges in the outer part of the atmosphere, was left to our century.

The observations carried out at the new permanent stations in Toronto and Hobart provided Sir Edward Sabine, a geophysicist well-known for his gravimetric and magnetic measurements in the Arctic, with the data for a thorough analysis of the occurrence of magnetic storms. As a result, he could show that these sudden disturbances possess a periodi/ city which coincides with that of the fluctuating sunspot activity. The extra/terrestrial origin of magnetic storms which had been demonstrated by their simultaneous occurrence over a wide area of the earth, had now been traced to its source.

In addition to his efforts at an extension of the magnetic observatories and in addition to his work on the results of his Siberian expedition, Humboldt finished in these years two very disparate books, disparate in contents and in treatment. The first of these appeared in 1836 and represented the last instalment of his South American publications, a history of the discovery of America, or, to give it its full title, 'critical examination of the history of geography of the new continent and of the progress of nautical astronomy in the fifteenth and sixteenth century'. His stay in Madrid and Mexico had given him access to documents which were then quite unknown in western Europe, and he had continued to collect material in the following thirty years. In the course of these investigations, he had been fortunate enough to discover in the library of Baron Walckenaer, a member of the *Institut*, one of the earliest known maps of the new world which had been drawn in 1500 by Juan de la Cosa, one of the companions of Columbus on his second expedition and who had sailed in 1499 with Amerigo Vespucci. But Humboldt had been overtaken by events; Navarete's work on the Spanish voyages and dis/ coveries in the fifteenth century had been published in 1825.

'Coldly boring' was Humboldt's own verdict on his long delayed book: 'It is one of the most ill/composed German works (and that means something); I feel it and I know it but I believe that my book contains entirely new material and that the erudition is not trivial; the combination of physical and historical knowledge imparts character to it but the lack of division into chapters is supremely boring for the reader, and in these eternal and interminable sections, a little vivacity of style

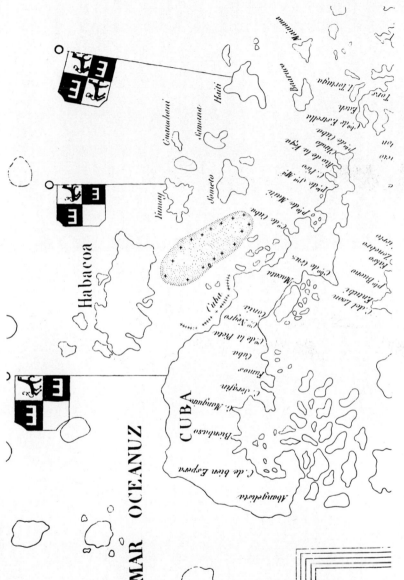

VI. Section from Juan de la Cosa's map (1500) showing the position of Guanahani, the site of Columbus's landfall

is of no avail in forming a whole of seemingly disconnected pieces.'[9] Humboldt showed himself here a remarkably accurate judge of his own work; the book exhibits scarcely any organization. His erudition thoroughly got the better of him; the text is swamped by footnotes. Every allusion to a country in the west is pursued through classical and medieval sources before the main theme is approached. Arago once said of Humboldt's books that they are pictures without a frame but rather they resemble the exploration of a vast river system where every tributary of a tributary is followed right up to its source. It is very difficult in the end to tell the main stream from the side issues. He was incapable of leaving anything out.

The contents of the 'Critical Examination' can be summarised under three main headings: first, the events preceding and leading up to the discovery of America, secondly, some biographical data on Columbus and Amerigo Vespucci, and thirdly, the first maps of the new world and the appearance of the name 'America'. A projected fourth section, the discussion of the history of nautical astronomy and the design of maps in the fifteenth and sixteenth centuries, was never published, although it is promised at the beginning of the book. Humboldt had worked on the material for nearly thirty years; as he admits himself at the end, he had changed his opinions while he was writing. Unfortunately, he did not revise it when it was finished. Fascinating as some of the sidelines are, their relevancy to the main theme is not easy to see. The history of the magnetic compass from ancient China to the Catalan sailors of the Middle Ages is not inapposite but it is rather obscure where an account of the fermentation and distillation of mare's milk comes in.

A great admiration for the enterprise and persistence of Columbus is combined with discernment of the consequences for the intellectual development of western Europe. 'The discovery of the new continent and the efforts made to extend the knowledge of its geography have not only lifted the veil which for centuries had covered a vast part of the surface of the earth; this discovery and these efforts have had the most marked influence on the improvement of maps and graphical methods in general as well as on the astronomical methods of deter/mining geographical positions. Studying the progress of civilisation, we see everywhere how the sagacity of man grows with the field opening out to his research. Nautical astronomy, physical geography (including under this term notions on the varieties of human species and the distribution of plants and animals), the geology of volcanoes, descriptive natural history, all these branches of science have changed their appearance since the end of the fifteenth and the beginning of the sixteenth century. Never since the beginning of organised society had the sphere of ideas about the external world grown in such a pro/digious manner; never had man felt a more pressing need to observe nature and to multiply the means for successful investigation.'[10]

Since it is one of the main themes of the book to refute the idea that Vespucci had arrogated to himself the discovery of America, Humboldt recapitulates the documentary evidence of Columbus's expeditions, mainly on the basis of Navarete's publication. Admirer as he is of Columbus's genius and per/severance, he is perturbed by his inhumanity which allowed him to sell Indians like cattle. 'In Columbus are revealed, side by side with the individual originality of his character, the effect of the predominant doctrines of his time, doctrines which prepared by inhuman laws the expulsion of two entire races, the Moors and the Jews. Examining the causes of this religious intolerance, one is forced to admit that the fanaticism of this period, in spite of its violence, did no longer possess the can/dour of an exalted emotion. Involved in all the material inter/ests and vices of society, it was guided, in particular in the men in power, by a sordid avarice, by the necessities and quan/daries which were the origin of an uneasy and tortuous policy, of distant expeditions and the dilapidation of the finances of the state. The great complications of position and duties imposed by the court tended imperceptibly to vitiate the most generous minds. Highly placed individuals who depended on the favour of the government, based their actions on the opinions of their century and the principles which the authority of the sovereign seemed to justify. The crimes which have sullied the annals of mankind in the conquest of America after Columbus's death, had their mainspring less in the rudeness of customs and the ardour of passion than in the cold calculations of cupidity, in an over-sensitive prudence and in that excess of rigour which has been enforced at all times under the pretext of strengthening authority and consolidating the social structure.'[11]

The history of the introduction of slavery is now pursued in some detail. The struggle between the Christian principle of individual freedom and political and economic expediency is reflected in contradictory royal decrees; the instructions of the church were not without ambiguity either. Even Cortez admitted in his testament that he had been unable to resolve his doubts whether slaves could be kept in possession without remorse, and recommended to his son to find out the truth for the sake of his conscience. The doubts were there but slavery stayed until the liberation of the South American countries.

I have here discussed a matter which, until now, has not been tackled with the independence of mind which is demanded by the larger interests of humanity at every historical era. It is not the question of a bitter indict-ment or a timid defence of men who enjoy a well-merited reputation; it is the question of disseminating a juster opinion of the circumstances which introduced and maintained serfdom in America over a long period and under different denominations, circumstances which have presented themselves everywhere, from the middle ages to the present time, and which have led to equally disastrous results whatever the degree of intellectual culture of the so-called civilizing conquerors. . . . This analogy is proved not only by the accomplished facts, by the barbarous acts or by long oppression; it also shows in the arguments used to justify these acts, in the hatred towards those who denounce them, in the hesitant opinions and doubts to which people pretend in the choice between the just and unjust, the better to disguise their taste for servitude and rigorous measures.[12]

Humboldt's discovery of Juan de la Cosa's map of the New World, which bears the date of 1500, made a decisive contribution to the debate on the site of the first landfall of Columbus. Navarete had maintained that Columbus's island Guanahani, renamed by him San Salvador, was identical with one of the Turk Islands, most probably Grand Turk; while Muñoz, who had published his *History of the New World* in 1793, had concluded from the internal evidence of the original documents that Watling Island of the Bahamas was a much more likely choice, in agreement with present-day opinion. A detailed analysis of the descriptions of Columbus's route was given by Washington Irving in his work on the great navigator, which proved that all indications pointed to the Bahamas, and in his view to Cat Island. The position of Guanahani on Juan de la Cosa's map as well as on that by Diego Ribero of 1529 in the possession of the library at Weimar, provided documentary proof for the identification of Guanahani with one of the Bahamas islands. Humboldt himself inclined towards Watling Island.

The strange problem of how the new continent came to be named after Amerigo Vespucci, who had by no means been instrumental in its discovery, found its final solution in the 'Critical Examination'. Columbus, of course, never realized that he had not landed on the eastern coast of Asia; but neither did Vespucci who, as Humboldt says, 'shines only in the reflected light of a century of glory. Compared with Columbus, Sebastian Cabot, Bartholomew Diaz and Gama, Pinzon even, his is an inferior place.' Washington Irving had been the first to trace the earliest appearance of the name 'America' to an anonymous publication of the year 1507, the 'Introduction to cosmography with some necessary geometrical and astronomical principles, also the four navigations of Amerigo

Vespucci'. These four navigations are the Latin versions of four letters purporting to have been written by Vespucci to a member of the Medici family in Florence, of which editions in other languages exist. The original documents have never come to light and their authenticity seems somewhat doubtful when it is remembered that independent evidence indicates the presence of Vespucci only in the second and third expeditions of the four described in these letters.

The 'Introduction to Cosmography', originally printed in Sanctus Deodatus, was published in 1509 in Strasbourg, giving its author's name as Martinus Ilacomylus. It was Humboldt's achievement to establish the identity of Ilacomylus or Hylacomylus—both versions occur—with that of Martin Waldseemüller* who had been a student of the university of Freiburg in south Germany, and who had lived in St Dié in the Vosges, the Sanctus Deodatus of the 'Cosmography', a small town in the domain of the Duke of Lorraine of the time, René II, who had turned his country into a centre of geographical studies. It is highly unlikely that Vespucci ever saw this publication.

From this corner of Europe, the name of America for the newly-discovered world spread to maps, printed in southern Germany and Switzerland, and thus passed gradually into general use. It is one of the ironies of history that a whole continent was named by an obscure scholar of geography in an out-of-the-way town, not so far distinguished for anything else.

Humboldt was inordinately proud of this excursion into the field of textual analysis, so far removed from his scientific activities; his exhaustive discussion of all the relevant sources of information about the first discovery of the American continent has been a major contribution to European knowledge in the last century. It has, in fact, become part of our heritage, although his conviction that Vespucci was a member of all the

---

* A name of which Hylacomylus is a Greek version. The name 'America' had been suggested to Waldseemüller by his friend Mathias Ringmann.

four expeditions described in his letters has no longer any adherents.

After the publication of the 'Critical Examination', Hum/boldt returned to a theme to which he had first directed his attention in his book on Mexico, the movement of the precious metals, a statistical survey of the flow of silver and gold throughout the inhabited world since the conquest of America and the consequent opening of this main source of supply of currency. The secretiveness of the Spanish and Portuguese governments had successfully hidden from the rest of Europe how much bullion and coinage they actually imported from their American possessions. The statistical tables, published in the 'Political Essay', were the first reliable information on the production of gold and silver during a period of three hundred years. With a knowledge of the cost of European imports from Asia, it had been possible for Humboldt to calculate the amount of precious metals which had accumu/lated in the western world, an accumulation which included jewellery and plate. To assess the relative proportions, he had assumed that the figures available for France applied equally for the rest of Europe, a not very valid proceeding. At that time, however, he was unable to procure the necessary data in his Parisian isolation, behind the barrier of the continental blockade. With his predilection for graphical representation, he had originally intended to draw the lines of flow of gold on a map of the world 'like the map of Cook's journey' but had confined himself in the end to the orthodox and less costly tables.

With the beginning of the wars of independence in Central and South America in 1810, the import of metallic currency was gradually reduced; by 1820, it had fallen to less than half of the previous amount. At the same time, or more precisely since the conclusion of the Napoleonic wars, the continuous fall of prices had raised the problem of a possible causal con/nexion between those two phenomena. At the instigation of the former Chancellor of the Exchequer Huskisson, William Jacob undertook a new investigation; his book on the produc, duction and consumption of the precious metals was published in 1831. For accurate figures for the supply, he relied on Hum, boldt's statistics for the period before 1810 but was able to show that the losses had been completely counterbalanced by the rise of exports to the Asian countries in the 1820's, mainly from England and Russia. Thus the former trend of a drain of gold and silver towards the East had been reversed into a flow towards Europe in spite of the ever-growing imports of tea and spices. Although Jacob did not commit himself to a final statement, he implied a causal connexion between the fall in prices and the reduced production of the South American mines, in direct contradiction to his own researches.

The apprehensions of an insufficient supply of bullion, occasioned in financial circles by Jacob's publication, very soon gave way to the reverse panic at the discovery of important deposits of gold in North America and Siberia. The fears of a devaluation induced Humboldt to write an essay on the 'Fluc, tuations of Gold' which appeared in 1838. He provided new statistical tables of the amounts mined in Russia and the United States during the 1830s which were negligible com, pared with the quantities accumulated in the western world; the anxieties were seen to be baseless when the actual figures were consulted.

The flow of the precious metals from Asia or America to our smaller continent, and from it partially back again to the parent source, follows, like fluids, the laws of equilibrium. Under the influence of European demand there flows from Nerchinsk, the Urals and the Altay on one side, and from the mines of the United States on the other, a continuous stream of the precious metals; their exchangeable value, whether we con, sider the metals in relation to each other or as the measure of the price of commodities, is by no means entirely or principally determined by the decrease or increase of production. This exchangeable value is affected in an unequal degree by the complicated arrangements and fluctuating relations of modern societies, by an increasing or decreasing population and its progress in civilization, by the demand (regulated by the population) for a greater monetary circulation, by the frequently recurring necessity of remittances of bullion as well as by their destination, by the unequal wear and tear of the two precious metals, by the amount of paper money as part of the circulating medium, which all react on the metallic medium of exchange. A rise in the relative value of gold as compared with that of silver may as easily occur during a general increase in production as a temporary depression of the barometer and a rise in temperature with a strong north-east wind. In meteorological changes as well as in the exchange of precious metals, many factors are simultaneously at work. The effect of each individual cause, in raising or lowering prices, may be determinable, but not that of a combination of causes; their infinite number, their cumulative action, the fact that they partially cancel each other will defeat any *a priori* attempt to decide their aggregate influence.

Any increase in the production of the precious metals would seem infinitely unimportant compared with the accumulation of thousands of years now in circulation, especially when we consider the relative proportions between coins and jewellery and plate. Every increase, however inconsiderable, has an effect in the long run; but a perceptible deficiency may occur in the middle of an increasing supply since a growing population demands an enlarged circulation of money.[13]

The warning, justified as it has proved to have been, did not prevent a new and equally baseless panic at the discovery of gold in California and Australia in the 1850s.

Thirteen

THE EIGHTEEN-FORTIES

THE death of William IV had grave repercussions in the political and intellectual life of Germany; the Duke of Cumberland, Ernest Augustus, became King of Hanover and took immediate steps to suspend the only recently introduced constitution. The university of Göttingen, where the king himself had been a student, was in an uproar. A number of professors made violent objections; the more determined of them, seven altogether, were dismissed from their posts, among them the brothers Grimm of the fairy tales and the physicist Weber. Gauss, conservative and not very politically minded, came to an arrangement with his conscience and his monarch. Humboldt was overwhelmed with letters demanding help for the unfortunate victims of their convictions. 'The ferocious destruction of Göttingen, the desire to be of service to the expelled has been very much in my mind. Things are in a very bad state in Göttingen; it seems that everybody wants to emigrate. It is desolating and atrocious. They would like to destroy the universities; there still remains a passably ancient institution, continually renewed, and commonly called youth. How convenient it would be if youth could be abolished.'[1] There followed endless negotiations. The Prussian king, urged by Humboldt, permitted the admission of the Göttingen professors to university posts in his country, provided that posts became vacant. In the end, one professorship was found in Bonn, and the brothers Grimm, who were as inseparable as any old married couple, were called to Berlin as members of the academy with a fixed annual income. Nearly four years passed before the Minister of Education had unwound the right amount of red tape. With all the delays, the government did not behave ungenerously in a country which kept its own constitutionalists in prison or at least under strict police surveillance.

Ernest Augustus never forgave Humboldt for his successful intervention, and Humboldt loved to talk about the royal fury: 'If I were in his power, he would have me hanged and that to-day rather than to-morrow. I have confronted him several times here (in Berlin) and at Potsdam, and he knows that three of the Göttingen professors obtained their positions in this country mainly through my mediation. He cannot forget that. Once, he came straight out with it. Well, Humboldt, still a republican and that at Sans-Souci? Bothered about professors. They are in cheap supply like workmen and the persons whom the French call *putains*. They are cheap. But I said to him: that is not so. You made great efforts and could not get anybody for all your money. He has been angry ever since and would dearly like to hang me.'²

Oscillating between Berlin and Potsdam, Humboldt con-tinued to divide his life between his attendance at court and his writing-desk. His books, his correspondence had to be left to the nights. New editions of his earlier writings and the five volumes of his great work *Cosmos* testify to his vitality which allowed him, a man in his seventies, to stand on his feet for six to seven hours during the day and left him the energy and enthusiasm to sit over his papers for the better part of the night, to see his friends and his brother's children. He never forgot their birthdays, and from his longed-for visits in Paris, he always returned with presents for his nieces, the right kind of presents, bottles of scent, gloves and French chocolates. Artists and scientists appeal to him; Victor Hugo sends copies of his works for the hands of the Prussian king. Balzac comes to Berlin and Humboldt arranges for him a dinner invitation to Potsdam. A foreign associateship becomes vacant at the Paris *Institut* through the death of his old professor Blumenbach, the naturalist and physiologist, and Humboldt takes a hand in the election of a successor, proposing the names of Faraday, Oersted, Herschel, Bessel or Jacobi to Arago, a proposal which he follows up with a letter of warm recommendation for his old friend Buch:

You know that I have not been very successful in the elections of the last years and as far as a friendly appeal to you is concerned, it seems to me the more unnecessary as we always meet on the same paths without having to explain, attached as we are to each other and sharing the same predilections in fields where I am entitled to an opinion. In this position and in this affectionate acceptance of your will, I ask nothing of you. I know that you, with your extensive knowledge and your just appreciation of established reputations in Europe, will do what is right, or rather what can be done in the given circumstances. If a naturalist can only be replaced by a naturalist, then certainly, my preference would be for my oldest friend, Leopold von Buch, apart from the two botanists already on the list for the associateship. Geology deserves to be represented. It has made immense progress, it has undergone a complete revolution, and this auspicious revolution is almost entirely due to Buch. There is nobody, among living geologists, superior to Buch. He has made important expeditions north and south, to Lapland, the Canaries, Sicily and Greece. He has given proof of a long and courageous patience, travelling on foot through the mountains, hammer in hand, for forty years on end and 7-8 months every year. Moreover, he has had an important influence on the progress of meteorology (continental and sea climates, limits of eternal snow in the north) and on the geography of plants. I have sometimes for reasons derived from modern physics and chemistry, not been able to subscribe to his all too absolute doctrines but his views are always large, intelligent and productive. M. Laplace (if it is the question of a German) would have despised Buch because he had no idea of present-day geology, he would have wanted Bessel. I find much more originality in Buch, the creation of a science is here in question. Hutton was obviously on the way to a great number of things which we know to-day or believe (memoir on the granite 1785, theory 1795). I consider it a great misfortune that I had not read Hutton before my departure for America, as a mining director in a granitic country; but at that time, the phenomena did not seem to be connected, one could

believe in local exceptions. The difference between eruptive and sedimentary rocks, the certainty that the former are newer, have only become
universal in the last twenty years; it has followed on the successful
application of zoological features to the differentiation of sedimentary
rocks. Combinatory sciences are not created all at once.

But is a geologist acceptable and a *Prussian* geologist? Buch is so much
convinced that he is not wanted that in my last letter you will not even
find his name on my long list of prophesies. He had made me promise
'never to mention his name'; I should moreover remind you that a
number of years ago he had already begged you, my dear friend, or Gay
Lussac, to let his name disappear from the list. I told him that that was
unfair and inconvenient at the same time but I promised that I would
not interfere in what he calls 'his own affairs'. You know the originality
of this character: irritable, good and ferocious all at once. Since then,
letters from Elie de Beaumont to him and to me, urging Buch to take
steps *himself*, to send some publications to his friends in Paris!! have
exposed me to some feverish effusions. A complete isolation increases his
irritability. Mr. Buch is very transparent. He wants the impossible; he
would be very pleased to be elected without having his name on a list;
he refuses to see that the majority is a matter of luck in a battle where so
heterogeneous fighters engage in a fight that there is no reason to be
offended if a man is not elected but has the honour to find himself on
the list. He need not take any steps, certainly; he will be remembered as
long as geology is remembered, a science whose development is one of
the glories of our time.

My friend is fortunate enough to have inspired in you respect for him,
you know perfectly well what is owing to him, you have defended him
before with your eloquent and successful fervour, but I should not be at
all surprised to hear that your choice has gone elsewhere. I suspect the
African (Herschel) who, in spite of his erudition and the observations
and children he has made at the Cape and the star he has seen swell up
but not deflate and the 2463 double stars and the little photogenic papers
à la Talbot, appears to me inferior to the originality of his father, astronomer, physicist and poetical cosmologist all at once.

Faraday and Brewster! . . . The former bores me with his 2400 paragraphs which, he thinks, are all the same memoir. *You know* better than
anybody that not all that is claimed for him, is by him and certainly
not by him alone. I am even less in favour of Oersted who happened to

be lucky one day and has not had a long line of ingenious investigations such as have led Daguerre to his great discovery, so pregnant for the future (what style!).

It is truly perfidious to put the living side by side with those they have succeeded in the booklet of the *Institut*. I implore you to look at page 81. When you substitute Gauss or Berzelius for Banks, what a world then and to-day. Whoever knows something about science, must admit that it has sadly degenerated. There are only Berzelius, Gauss and Brown among the present, and Brown has had the misfortune to be a contemporary of Jussieu. I have a horrible spectre by my side, Cavendish.* I am comforted to think that I represent Bonpland at the *Institut*.

This is a very imprudent letter, if other people saw it; I know it will do me no harm with you. You like it if I am frank and you know perfectly well that, if I am rather severe on great men for whom I feel less liking than for Priestley, Cavendish, Herschel the father, Young, Wollaston, Davy, and if I appear conceited and arrogant, I have a very good idea how much I owe to a combination of fortunate circumstances, to influential friends, to a moderate mixture of miscellaneous knowledge and keenness of observation of which I have given proof; their results have never been sufficiently important to rouse the susceptibilities of better men. With a patience for longevity (one of the least meritorious elements of celebrity, but one of the most productive), I enjoy what I have fairly honestly acquired without being able to account in detail for the good fortune I have had.[3]

Buch was nominated and elected with an overwhelming majority, thirty-eight votes out of fifty-two. 'Buch and I have been overjoyed by your letter. . . . The poor nominee was feverishly uncertain. All the time he pretended (from a not quite convincing modesty) that he was more frightened to get in than to be defeated. As the danger came near, he went on a visit to his fields (he has inherited another estate, worth about £6,000 through the death of a brother). The cabbages did not soothe him and he came back to town, and since yesterday and the arrival of your kind letter, he has dropped his antics of a geologico-subterranean modesty and is frankly and effusively

* Humboldt had been the successor of Cavendish as foreign associate.

happy. He is happy, he is grateful to you, he says so to every-body, he behaves as he should after such a success.'[4]

The king, Frederick William III, died in the spring of 1840, succeeded by his eldest son, Frederick William IV. The suc-cession did not affect Humboldt's position, though naturally enough he felt the personal loss. 'I should have been ingrateful indeed not to have been affected by the loss of the king who had fine moral qualities, an honest man on the throne who has shown me many kindnesses. He left me the independence of my opinions and respected my attachment to friends whose ideas he found displeasing. . . . I am established with the new king in Sans-Souci where we shall remain for part of the sum-mer. The new king continues to show me the affection and confidence with which he had honoured me as crown prince. We pass the evenings on the historic little hill in a philosophical and literary solitude.'[5]

The progressively-minded had had great expectations of the new man on the throne, foremost the granting of the constitu-tion for which the war against Napoleon had been fought. But political decisions were not to the liking of Frederick William IV, who was a reactionary romantic with a preference for un-realistic dreams of a reunion of the Christian churches. He spent his time designing Gothic horrors and artificial ruins and planning a fantastic pilgrimage to Jerusalem. The 'Ultras', the orthodox churchmen and the members of the aristocratic families who had not liked the trend of the times, the partial loss of their economic and political privileges, very soon gathered round him and tried to take up the political reins. He had made a not inauspicious start: three Göttingen professors had been found positions in Prussia and a political amnesty had been declared which released a number of writers and students from prison or police supervision. Many of them were patriots of the Napoleonic wars, men who had organized the resistance against the French before 1813 and who had made too loud and too persistent demands for a constitution and political rights after 1815. Humboldt was made a member of the Privy Council, and the censorship of the press and of publications was partly removed. The king was so offended by the resultant expressions of discontent with public affairs that measures for the suppression of unorthodox and irreverent opinions were soon in force again. 'Freedom of thought is enjoyed by the people, by the masses,' said Heine, 'restriction strikes only at the small number of those who try to publish.'

Foreign affairs were dominated by the developments in the Near East, and the threat of war with France. England, Prussia, Austria and Russia were once again united against France over the invasion of Syria by Egyptian troops, a revolt of the ruler of Egypt against his Turkish overlord. The old Holy Alliance sought to keep the Ottoman empire in being while France was gaining influence in Egypt by favouring the first symptoms of Arab nationalism. The situation roused strong feelings of nationalism in Prussia, nearly as strong as those of 1813, which, as in 1813, found their expression in warlike poems, the famous 'Watch on the Rhine' among them. In the end, peace was preserved; the Egyptian troops were beaten and withdrawn and the four European powers, together with a reconciled France, signed in July 1841 the Convention of the Straits. Humboldt had been greatly distressed by this development; he was a peace-loving man and convinced that any country gained greater glory by its artistic and technical achievements than by military victories. Added to that, there was his personal attach-ment to Arago, and the fear that politics would put a barrier between them. 'I am longing to see you again; if my health remains good, I should like to start for Paris early in the spring and stay for some months; I am saddened by the uncertainty that this stay which promises so much pleasure for me on account of the observatory *alone*, could be inconvenient for you and less agreeable than at former times in our lives. I would not even have the courage to give up this plan of an old man; I must profit from the time still left to me, but incapable of doing anything that could displease you in the complicated situation, accustomed to look upon your slightest wish as an order, I should be happy if you would have the kindness to send me three lines. It would be sufficient to say: "*I shall see you arrive with the same pleasure as before.*" Can you refuse me this kindness? It would be the nicest present from you for the new year. My life like yours has been tumultuous. I am also tor-mented by correspondence and solicitations to which I cannot do justice. I only work without disturbance at night, from 9 until 2 o'clock. I still go to bed very late.'[6] Arago replied, three months later: 'I cannot, I will not believe that you can ask *seriously* whether I should find pleasure in your journey to Paris. Do you really feel doubt in my attachment? Any un-certainty on this point would be cruelly wrong. Apart from my family, you are beyond comparison the person I love most in the world. You are the only one of my friends on whom I would count in a difficult situation. I am truly happy to think that I shall spend some evenings with the man to whom I owe my taste for meteorology and geophysics. You can have a bed at the observatory. You will arrive in time for my course on astronomy. My new lecture theatre is scandalously luxurious.'[7]

This is one of the few letters from Arago to Humboldt which have been preserved; Humboldt, who was not a posses-sive person, destroyed his correspondence with the exception of the papers which he presented to Varnhagen for his collection of autographs. Among those was this declaration of Arago's friendship with the request not to publish it before the death of the writer.

After his return from Paris, Humboldt found the pietistic tendencies of the court and the politically ambitious more dis-tasteful than ever. Under the influence of one of the more ardent enthusiasts, Josiah von Bunsen, who had recently become Prussian envoy in London, the king had decided to attend the christening of the Prince of Wales, the future king Edward VII, a plan which filled the progressively-minded with misgivings. Varnhagen noted in his diary: 'I heard to-day, in confidence, the queer myth that the king is going to England, to the christening of the Prince of Wales; the visit has been negotiated in secret and the flattering information has helped to make the nomination of Bunsen acceptable to the English court. The whole story is suspect. Diplomatic relations are not like that. But if there is a foundation in it, Bunsen must have taken a hand and there may be great consequences. In my opinion, dangerous consequences; a close link with England would be of doubtful value but a close affiliation with the Tories and the Anglican church—a real disaster. And every-body in Prussia, in Germany, in Europe would assume such a connection as certain even if it did not come to pass. It would do untold damage; the king would lose more in popularity than he can afford to lose now. I hope the whole story is a fabrication.'[8]

It was no fabrication, but it had no political consequences either. Frederick William IV, accompanied by Humboldt, went to Windsor early in 1842. The execrable lines written by Leigh Hunt in celebration of the happy event—'and the genial king with the wise companioning'—are supposed to allude to the presence of the Prussian monarch and his scientific adviser. Humboldt had not been overjoyed at the prospect of this journey: 'This duty is not at all my business; my position at the court is quite independent but I cannot refuse it to the claims of friendship, even of a gentle and witty tyrant. I shall not get any intellectual pleasure out of a journey of this kind.' His social obligations did not allow him a single visit to the observatory at Greenwich. His impressions are preserved in Varnhagen's invaluable diary: 'Humboldt talked very inter-estingly about England. At the court, great splendour, but a simple and natural way of life, the conversation easy, the tone very friendly and good-natured, even among men and women of very different opinions. He dislikes Peel more than ever, he looks like a Dutchman, is more vain than ambitious, petty in outlook. Lord Aberdeen is mulishly silent but does not manage to convey that he is capable of saying something clever if he would speak. Bunsen committed the greatest blunders; all the world is against him, only the king more than ever for him. Even the English say that the whole journey was nothing but an intrigue of Bunsen.'⁹

The king had soon found a new plaything; he added a divi-sion to the order of merit which had been founded by Frederick the Great as a reward for military services, and which was now to be conferred as well for artistic and scientific achievements. Humboldt was appointed chancellor of the new knighthood, and the king himself drew up the lists of the first members to be elected with a fine international impartiality. For weeks he played with his toy, erasing names and adding others, and to keep his efforts secret from his surroundings, he used the Indian alphabet. The decoration was not always well received; Manzoni went so far as to refuse it outright, for political reasons, and it became Humboldt's unpleasant duty to soothe the king and humour Manzoni. He had himself very little understand-ing for the delight of eminent people in 'glass buttons, peacock feathers and coloured ribbons'. He was also frightened that Arago would feel impelled to tread in Manzoni's footsteps.

The letter I write to-day, has a great importance for my political position. I have a request, a humble request, I need two lines from your hand before your departure to the eclipse in Perpignan. I believe too much in your goodwill towards me to fear for a moment that you will put me in the most painful position. I implore you *not to refuse*. This is the position: to-day is the 102nd anniversary of the coronation of the philosopher-king whom we call the great Frederick. Our present king has had the idea that one could not object to ally to the name of his fore-father all that is eminent in intellectual achievements. This order of merit, created in 1740 and which Frederick II had conferred upon Voltaire, d'Alembert, the Marquis d'Argens, and which since has been only given to military people, has been restored for the sciences, literature and the arts. It is the intention to unite in this new division of the order of Frederick the Great the great luminaries of Europe, completely inde/ pendent of political ideas. The king thinks that a great name like yours should open the list of foreign members. The *ultra* party which is very strong, has been very vocal: favouring democracy, offending King Louis Philippe.—'I have defended your friend,' says the king, 'Arago's opinions of the regime of his country are not my concern, I have no right to judge. If O'Connell had made the same discoveries, I should not hesitate to nominate him.' The *conservatives* have been in an uproar, against the king, against me. Your name has been gazetted to/day together with the names of Chateaubriand, Ingres, Horace Vernet (who painted the battle of Jena), Melloni, Meyerbeer, Rossini, the poet Thomas Moore, who has written a satirical poem on Prussia and the Holy Alliance, Faraday, Herschel, Robert Brown, Berzelius, Daguerre. You are not in unworthy company. You will presently receive the decoration with the cipher of Frederick II and an accompanying letter. I am mort/ ally afraid that you will not be pleased, my dear friend. But I have not had the courage to say to the king: it will cause him pain. After fighting for him at Potsdam, you may have the disappointment that M. Arago, in a republican convulsion, returns the decoration or does not even ack/ nowledge receipt. It is a nightmare. I remember the Belgian decoration. Here I am on my knees before you, I pray for the help of your sister and of the angel of harmony. All I ask is that you fill in a form which says simply: François Arago, born at Perpignan, perpetual secretary of the academy of sciences. It is an engraved picture in which you write your name and the date of your birth.

It is not even necessary to write to the king. All I want is just two lines addressed to me with the words: Thank you for the honour to see my name on the list; and it will never be in the papers that you have accepted. It is more like an academy than a decoration, you need not show the *object* to anybody. Your predecessor d'Alembert has had it; don't be fierce and if you feel inclined not to accept, not to reply to me, do stop to think of the cruel position in which I should be placed here. Do comfort me before you receive the miserable thing, it may be weeks. To adore my friends and to be frightened at my age. It is miserable.[10]

Arago behaved; but Humboldt felt increasingly dissatisfied with his existence, 'on the evening of an agitated and yet not really fulfilled life'. The political developments were less and less to his liking. Instead of an elected parliament, the people were given a form of corporate representation, provincial estates, to be convened only every four years. The king would not tolerate a written constitution to come 'between the Lord and this country'. The *ultras* invaded the cabinet, the higher administrative posts and the court, where they made front against Humboldt. 'I live, under the outward appearance of splendour and the predilection of the monarch, in a moral solitude as only the dour mentality of this country can produce.' He tells Varnhagen that, without his standing at court, he would be expelled from the country by the intrigues of the *ultras* and the pietists, and there would not be a place in the other German states where he would be tolerated if he lost the glamour and the protection of his position: he even began to play with the idea of emigration.

Humboldt's only relief in these more and more oppressive times were his frequent visits to Paris and to Arago, where, in 1845, Sir James Hooker, the botanist, made his acquaintance. Hooker, who had taken part in the Antarctic expedition under the command of Ross as ship's surgeon, was then in the first flush of success; his *Antarctic Flora* marked the beginning of a long and extremely distinguished career; Humboldt, with his usual eager interest, had hundreds of questions about the journey and its scientific results. His personal appearance was a sad disenchantment for the young man who described it to his mother: 'On putting up here I sent in my card with Mr. Brown's book to Baron Humboldt; he was not at home but sent his flunkey (Scoticè Footman) to my bedroom at 8 o'clock yesterday morning to say his master wished to see me at 9. Ten minutes after his Lord had grown impatient and sent to say he was all ready, so I went in and saw to my horror a *paunchy little German* instead of a Humboldt. There was no mistaking his head, however, which is exceedingly like all the portraits though now powdered with white. I expected to see a fine fellow, six feet without his boots, who would make as few steps to get up Chimborazo as thoughts to solve a problem. I cannot now at all fancy his trotting along the Cordillera as I once supposed he would have stalked.'[11] His mind though was all that he had imagined. There have been others who, on first meeting Humboldt, were disappointed at his relatively small stature and insignificant appearance. The disappoint-ment soon vanished when Humboldt talked, and all im-pressions became centred on his mobile features, expressive mouth and brilliant eyes, 'the eyes of an intelligent woman'.

The political situation in Prussia as elsewhere grew more and more ominous; the discontent of the professional and middle classes was sharpened by the economic distress of the smallholders and day labourers in the hungry forties. In com-mon with the small artisans and the increasing industrial proletariat, they were literally starving to death, after a series of bad harvests and rising food prices. In the spring of 1847 already, Humboldt was beginning to expect an open revolt. He was prepared for violence of every kind, for police action and the intervention of the army. The king was in high spirits, completely unaware of the growing opposition among the people.

The new surge of political consciousness everywhere in Europe lost Prussia her Swiss possessions; Neufchâtel expelled the Prussian governor and joined the Swiss Confederation in 1847. Poland was in ferment again; revolts broke out in the republic of Cracow, a creation of the wars against Napoleon, and spread to the Austrian province of Galicia. In the Prussian parts, east of the Oder, an open rebellion was prevented at the last moment by the arrest of the leaders. The Prussian liberals and Humboldt with them spoke publicly for the right of the Polish people to self-determination. Humboldt reports a strange remark of the Prince Consort to him in connexion with these events. In the course of a conversation at Stolzenfels, on the occasion of the visit of Queen Victoria to the Rhine in the sum-mer of 1846, Prince Albert said to the Prussian chamberlain:

'I know, you show much sympathy for the misfortunes of the Poles in Russia. Unfortunately, the Poles deserve as little sympathy as the Irish.' When, after the death of Humboldt, this statement was published, the *Edinburgh Review* exclaimed: 'It is difficult to conceive anything more ungracious or unjust. That the remark on the Russian Poles and the Irish was ever made in sober seriousness by His Royal Highness, is in the highest degree improbable.'[12] This seems to have been the first occasion on which a certain similarity between the Irish and the Polish character has been noticed.

In January 1848 Humboldt returned from a stay of three months in Paris for the very last time. In February, revolution broke out in Paris and in March in Berlin.

Fourteen

COSMOS

IN 1848, Humboldt had another eleven years of his very long life before him, years in which his physical activities became finally centred on Berlin and its surroundings. The political events much more than the natural decrease in his strength forced him into a static existence, foreign to his nature. Mentally, he was as active as ever; he went on working on his great work, *Cosmos*, revised new editions of his former books, wrote articles, and until the very end kept in touch with the latest developments of science.

The first volume of *Cosmos*, sketch for a physical description of the world, had been published in 1845. The second appeared in 1847, the third in 1850 and the fourth in 1858, and a fifth was printed from his notes after his death. It had been Humboldt's aim to give a scientifically accurate picture of the structure of the universe which would attract the general interest of the educated public and communicate some of the excitement of scientific study to the non-scientific mind. Since he saw nature as a whole and man as part of nature, and therefore all intellectual and artistic activities as having a share in natural history, he linked his main theme to an exposition of its development through the centuries and to the history of landscape painting and the descriptive poetry of nature. He had planned the book for nearly fifty years. In 1796, he had written: 'I have conceived the idea of a physics of the world. As I feel the increasing need for it, I see also how few foundations exist for such a vast edifice.'[1] The book, when it was finally completed, followed fairly faithfully the scheme of the course of lectures he had given in 1828. Since his return from Russia, he had divided his time between his other activities and *Cosmos*, although the greater part of the first volume in its ultimate form was written during the two years before its publication. The text contained factual information only and very few numerical data whose detailed discussion was left to appendices which gave at the same time the necessary references and accompanied every chapter. Humboldt was most scrupulous there; he circu-lated the proof sheets among all the authorities of the various special subjects touched upon for their comments and correc-tions. We owe to this procedure a major geomagnetic dis-covery: through such proof sheets, Sabine was informed of the observations of sun-spots by the amateur astronomer Schwabe which proved their periodicity and which provided Sabine with the evidence that allowed him to postulate the origin of magnetic storms in the fluctuating sun-spot activity. Hum-boldt's notes to *Cosmos* are for us an unparalleled source of information on the knowledge of his time in geophysics and astronomy.

A letter to Varnhagen, written in 1834, gives a fairly com-prehensive idea of Humboldt's intentions:

I begin the printing of my book (the work of my life). I have the crazy idea to represent in one work the whole material world, everything we know to-day of the phenomena in the celestial spaces and of life on earth, from the stars in the nebulae to the geography of mosses on granitic rocks, and in a book which stimulates by its lively language the imagina-tion. Together with the facts, every great and important idea which has come to light anywhere will be noted. It is meant to describe a chapter of the intellectual development of mankind (the knowledge of nature). The prolegomena are mainly finished: the whole redrafted opening discourse of my lectures, the picture of nature, the stimulants provided nowadays for the study of nature, first descriptive poetry and the vivid description of natural scenes in modern accounts of travels, secondly landscape painting, pictorial representations of an exotic nature, when it originated, when it became consequential, why antiquity with all its passions did not possess it, thirdly plant life, (parks) grouping the plants according to their physiognomy (not botanical gardens). A history of the physical

description of the world, how the idea of a universe, of the inter-connec-
tion of all phenomena has emerged in the course of the centuries. These
prolegomena are the cardinal point and constitute the general part; it is
followed by the particularisation. The universe—the whole physical
astronomy—our solid earth, inside, outside, the electromagnetism of the
interior. Volcanism, i.e. the reaction of the interior of the planet on its
surface. The structure of the solid masses. A little geology, the sea, the
atmosphere, climates, organisms, geography of plants. Geography of
animals, the human races and languages whose physical organisation
(the production of sounds) is regulated by the intellect. In the special part,
all the numerical results, the most accurate, as in Laplace's exposition
of the system of the world. Since these details do not fit stylistically into
the literary representation of the general account of our scientific knowledge, they will be stated in short sentences, almost like tables, so that
the reader will find compressed into a few sheets all the results about, for
instance, climatology or geomagnetism which only a prolonged study can
furnish otherwise. Cohesion with the general part is assured by means of
short introductions to every chapter.

I wanted to give you myself an idea of my plan. I did not succeed in
condensing the material into one volume although it would have been
more impressive. I hope that it will fill no more than two volumes. No
footnotes underneath the text but notes after every chapter which can be
left unread but which contain more details and sound knowledge. It is
not meant to be what is commonly called a physical description of the
earth, it comprises earth and sky, the whole creation. I had started fifteen
years ago to write it in French when I called it 'essay on the physics of
the world'. In Germany, I had at first intended to call it the book of
nature after Albertus Magnus in the middle ages. But it is all quite
undecided. At the moment, my title is 'Cosmos, sketch of a physical
description of the world.' I wanted to add the word 'Cosmos' to make
people call it by that name and not Humboldt's geophysical description.
My brother is in favour of the title 'Cosmos'; I have been rather hesitant.

Now my request to you, my dear friend. I cannot bear to send the
manuscript away before I have implored you to take a critical look at it.
You have so much talent for a graceful style, you have the wit and
understanding not to reject outright individual expressions which would
not be your own. Be kind enough to read the screed and to write on a
piece of paper without giving any reasons: so and so . . . I should prefer

to put. . . . But do not find fault without helping me. And give me some comfort over the title. The main defects of my style are an unfortunate inclination for too poetic forms, an overlong participial construction and a concentration of many opinions and sentiments into one sentence. I believe that these root evils are compensated by an earnest simplicity and penetration (a floating above the mere observation if I may be vain enough to say so). A book about nature should produce the impression of nature itself. One point I have paid particular attention to as in my 'Aspects of Nature' and that is where my manner differs completely from Chateaubriand and Forster, I have tried to be truthful in my description, scientifically true without going into the arid region of knowledge.[2]

The corrections proposed were gratefully and gracefully accepted by Humboldt: 'I have used everything, almost everything, more than 95 per cent. There is always a residue of obstinacy.'

The outline of the mid-nineteenth-century views of the structure of the universe, or as Humboldt called it, the picture of nature, presented in the first volume of *Cosmos*, is filled in in detail in the third and fourth, the astronomical section in the former and the geophysical in the latter. More than ten years lie between the publication of the first and the last part, and the care taken by the author to make use of the very latest results has left to us a fascinating record of the development during that period. The boldness of his enterprise had not escaped Humboldt's attention: 'On the evening of a much agitated life, I consign to the German public a work whose vaguely perceived image I have carried in my mind for almost half a century. There have been moments when I have felt the impossibility of its achievement, and after I had given it up, I have, perhaps imprudently, returned to it. I dedicate it to my contemporaries with the trepidation induced by a just mistrust in the measure of my strength. I seek to forget that a long expected publication will in general be met with less forbearance.'[3]

The defence of the intellectual charm of scientific study might still serve as a model: 'It is the particular aim of these conversations on nature to correct some of the errors which have sprung from a crude and incomplete empiricism and continue to live on in the higher classes of society (often side by side with an excellent literary education), and thus to increase by a deeper insight into its essence the enjoyment of nature. I cannot share the apprehension caused by a certain narrow-mindedness and clouded sentimentality that nature loses its magic, the charm of the mysterious and the sublime by any study of its forces. . . . To the physicist who (like Thomas Young, Arago and Fresnel) measures the unequal wave lengths of light, enhanced or destroyed by interference, to the astronomer who (like Herschel, South and Struve) uses the telescope to penetrate into space and to resolve the glimmer of a point of light into coloured double stars, to the experienced glance of the botanist who discovers the circulation of globules of sap in all vegetable cells, the morphological unit, is revealed more grandeur at the sight of the celestial spaces or the flowering plants on earth than to the observer whose feeling for nature has not been sharpened by an insight into the interrelation of phenomena. We cannot concur with Burke when he says that ignorance of nature only is the source of admiration and the feeling of the sublime.'[4]

Humboldt's considerations of the utilitarian necessity for a wider propagation of scientific knowledge are word for word the same as those which have led to the expansion of scientific education in these last years. He points to the fact that the general appreciation of all scientific studies is indispensable in a period in which the material wealth and growing prosperity of a nation are founded on the careful utilization of natural products and the forces of nature, that a glance at the state of the world proves that national wealth diminishes where this struggle for new technical processes is relaxed or halted. It is the fate of states that nature's curse falls on stagnation. Only a serious encouragement of mathematical, physical, chemical and other scientific studies can counteract such a regression. The intelligence of the people is power; knowledge and learning are an important part of the national wealth and a substitute for the often sparingly distributed natural resources. 'Those countries which lag behind in industry, in the application of mechanics and technical chemistry, in the careful selection and utilization of natural products, where the respect for such activities does not permeate all classes of society, will unfailingly decline in prosperity. They will sink faster when their neighbour states, with an energetic exchange between science and industry, go forward with renewed vitality.'[5]

He was firmly convinced that a predilection for industrial progress and for the scientific and technological knowledge which it demanded, could not be detrimental to philosophical and historical research nor could it rob the artist of his imagination. He believed that in a free and wisely governed country, where all human activities would be able to develop in peaceful competition, a dynamic balance between the two sides would be maintained to the benefit of the whole community.

The central idea of *Cosmos* is the scientific exposition of the nature with which we are all familiar, perceptible to our senses, and which so many, otherwise highly educated people, do not wish to have explained to them. From the starred sky above us to very nearly the moral law in us, the forces holding the organic and inorganic world together, are set out. All branches of science are involved and called in where they are applicable, from physics to anthropology. The historical sections of the second volume link the sciences to the arts and the humanities. The terrestrial section, the physical description of the earth, brings in all Humboldt's old favourites, the influence of the shape of the continents and the indentations of the coasts on the climate and the course of the isothermal lines, the alignment of volcanoes and the evolution of mountain ranges, the development of geomagnetic research and the geographical distribution of plant life, oceanic currents and their effects, all the subjects to which his own work had given a new direction. Faithful to his often-expressed aversion from any overt controversy, he passes over in silence ideas which he is unable to accept: the existence of glacial ages is not mentioned and the appearance of erratic blocks far from their original positions tentatively ascribed to the action of the waters released by the upheaval of mountain ranges.

Humboldt's account of the propagation of seismic waves has become the basis of modern seismology: 'Earthquakes are characterised by horizontal, vertical or rotatory vibrations which follow each other in quick succession. The waves are usually propagated in a linear direction with a velocity of 23 to 32 miles per minute, or in circles and large ellipses in which the vibrations spread as from a centre in decreasing amplitudes to the circumference. Some districts belong to two intersecting seismic circles. Where the seismic circles intersect, when for example a plateau lies between two volcanoes in simultaneous eruption, two wave systems can exist at the same time and, as in liquids, without mutual perturbation. Interference can also occur as in intersecting waves of sound.'[6]

'We cannot help supposing,' says the *Edinburgh Review*, 'the true mode of earthquake propagation (by waves of elastic compression) to have been apprehended with very considerable distinctness in penning this passage, though not seized and worked out, as it might have been, into a regular theory. We will only notice, in further illustration of the explanatory power of this mode of conceiving the matter, the facility with which the singular effect of vorticose motion is accounted for by the crossing of two waves of horizontal vibration which, as in the theory of the circular polarization of light, compound at their point of intersection a rotary movement. That a theory so simple, and we may add, so obvious, has not been earlier propounded and conceived, can only be accounted for by the vast scale of the phenomena and the amplitude of the earthquake wave itself which causes the wave itself as an advancing form to escape notice, and the molecular motions only by which it is propagated to be perceived.'[7]

With a discussion of the human races, Humboldt reaches the

boundary of the physical description of the world. Everything pertaining to the intellectual activities of human beings is out-side the scope of *Cosmos*, but a short sketch of the diversity of human races, of their geographical distribution, of their inter-action with their surroundings forms a necessary part of it. With all his adaptability, with his capacity to escape from the influence of natural forces and to use them for his own ends, man can never be wholly free of an organic dependence on the soil, on the climate and on his heredity like any other animal. At the time of the publication of the first volume of *Cosmos*, anthropologists still debated the question whether the human races belong to different genera or merely to different species. Humboldt expressed his conviction that they form one genus, a conviction based on his knowledge of the anatomy of racial characteristics and on the fact that all races can interbreed. He was rather scornful at the attempts to find the original seat of mankind from which all people were supposed to have spread over the world, although he did not deny that vast migrations had from time to time completely altered the geographical distribution of the human species; in fact, he was one of the first to suggest that the similarities between the American Indians and the Mongolians made it probable that the Americas had been populated by Mongolian tribes who had crossed from the northern coasts of Asia into Alaska. On the other hand, he warned against a too ready identification of language with race; languages also migrate. Sometimes they are imposed on conquered nations by the conquerors who may be small in number; sometimes, they follow in the wake of a new religion. Humboldt stresses the unity of mankind and rejects, as on other occasions, the concept of superior and inferior human races. He can only admit the distinction between nations of a higher culture, of an advanced intellectual development, and those in a more primitive state of civilization; there is no innate superiority. All of them he declares to be equally destined for freedom, individually and in groups.

The historical part of the second volume of *Cosmos* covers to a certain extent the same ground as the 'Critical Examination', the history of geographical discoveries from the time of the Egyptians to the achievements of the fifteenth and sixteenth centuries. It is followed by a survey of the development of astronomy and astronomical instruments and theory, physics and chemistry in connexion with geomagnetism, meteorology and geology right up to the end of the seventeenth century. It displays the full glory of Humboldt's enormous range of knowledge: the rôle of the Phoenicians and the Arabic civilization, Indian mathematics and the importance of Gilbert's contribution to our understanding of the geomagnetic field, wide acquaintance with the Greek and Latin sources, the medieval schoolmen and the great scientists of the sixteenth and seventeenth centuries, not to mention the mineralogical work of Nicholas Steno whose importance has been lately rediscovered.

With the discussion of descriptive poetry of nature and landscape painting, Humboldt passes from the objective to the subjective, from the realm of facts and figures to that of the emotions. It is his concern to trace the connexion between imaginative creations and the inclination to scientific studies, the intellectual stimulation through the arts which he had himself experienced. 'If I might call on my own recollections, if I ask myself what gave the first impulse to an ineradicable longing for tropical countries, I would have to name: George Forster's descriptions of the South Sea islands, a painting of the banks of the Ganges by Hodges in the house of Warren Hastings in London and a colossal dragon tree in an old tower of the botanical gardens in Berlin.'[8] With his highly developed historical sense and his passion for completeness, Humboldt sketches the evolution of the representation of nature in poetry and painting through the ages. His own enthusiasm for the beauty of tropical scenery convinced him that landscape painting would progress far beyond Poussin and Claude when once it became possible for artists to travel easily beyond the

European countries. His not unreasonable expectations have not been fulfilled. Landscape painting did indeed reach new heights in the nineteenth century but with the artists firmly bound to their native soil. The ties between the intellect and the impressions of the familiar seem to be a necessity for the painter. The one exception is Gauguin, and he had spent the first years of his life in Peru and was proud of his Inca lineage.

The scientific notes to *Cosmos* are a fascinating source of information on far-seeing intuitions as well as absurdities. There is Poisson's idea of an electrically charged layer beyond the limits of the atmosphere which foreshadows the modern concept of the ionosphere. He found it difficult to reconcile the great heights at which meteors become incandescent with the rarefication of the air. 'It seems difficult to attribute the incandescence of meteors as it is done, to the friction against the molecules of the air at a distance from the earth where the atmospheric density is negligibly small. It would be possible to assume that the electric fluid in a neutral state formed a kind of atmosphere extending far beyond the mass of air; although physically imponderable, it would be subject to the force of gravitation and follow the movements of the earth. According to this hypothesis, the meteors, entering this imponderable atmosphere, would decompose the neutral fluid by their unequal effect on the two kinds of electricity; by charging up, they would become hot and incandescent.'[9]

It is not often remembered that Arago's experiments on the refraction of star-light had led him to the conclusion that light is propagated through empty space with a constant velocity which is independent of the relative motion of the earth towards or away from the source of radiation. Fizeau's classical measurement of the speed of light was the immediate consequence of these observations. Although Humboldt was an adherent of Young's wave theory, he often added an interpretation in terms of Newton's theory of corpuscular emission to his explanations of optical phenomena; more than forty years after its inception, the wave theory was not so universally accepted as to be taken for granted. Humboldt quotes a very curious hypothesis which the followers of the emission theory had put forward to account for the existence of dark stars, a discovery which many astronomers found extremely disquieting. To explain the darkness away, it was assumed that these stars were luminous but of such size that the light corpuscles are bent back by the stellar gravitational field. According to Newton's theory, a star with the density of the sun and a diameter two hundred and fifty times bigger, would be invisible at large distances. 'The emission theory lends a scientific form to such phantasies.'

Cosmos cannot be said to be a work on popular science in the usual meaning of the word; its appeal was to a highly literate public, capable of following his allusions to the classics and to modern writers. It was, however, an enormous success even if Carlyle called it *dreich*. The first edition of the first volume was sold out in two months. It was immediately translated into nearly all European languages; the English version is by Sabine's wife, carried out under her husband's supervision. In 1851, Humboldt reports with pride that eighty thousand copies have been sold.

Exhaustive and favourable reviews appeared everywhere, wordy, eulogistic and lengthy enough to make the actual reading of the work under review almost superfluous. The *Quarterly* and the *Edinburgh Review* were united in praise. 'The author of the remarkable book before us is assuredly the person in all Europe best fitted to undertake and accomplish such a work. Science has produced no man of more rich and varied attainments, more versatile in genius, more indefatigable in application to all kinds of learning, more energetic in action, or more ardent in inquiry; and, we may add, more entirely devoted to her cause in every period of a long life. At every epoch of that life, from a comparatively early age, he has been constantly before the public, realising the ideal conception of a perfect traveller; a character which calls for almost as great a variety of excellencies as those which go to realise Cicero's idea of a perfect orator. To such a one science in all its branches must be familiar since questions of science and its applications occur at every step, and often in their most delicate and recondite forms. . . . To these must be added a knowledge of man and of his history in all its phases, social and political; a ready insight into human character and feelings, and a quick apprehension of local and national peculiarities. Above all things is necessary a genial and kindly temperament which excites no enmities but on the contrary finds or makes friends everywhere; in presence of which hearts open, information is volunteered and aid spontaneously offered. No man in the ranks of science is more distinguished for this last characteristic than Baron von Humboldt. We believe that he has not an enemy. His justice, candour and moderation have preserved him intact in all the vexatious questions of priority and precedence which agitate and harass the scientific world and have in consequence afforded him innumerable opportunities of promoting the objects and befriending the cultivators of science which would never have fallen in the way of a less conciliatory disposition, and of which he has not been slow to avail himself. The respect of Europe, indeed, has gone along with him to a point which has almost rendered his recommendations rules. It has sufficed that von Humboldt has pointed out lines of useful and available inquiries to make everyone eager to enter upon them.'[10]

The *Quarterly Review* paraphrases the same theme as its northern rival:

No human being breathes who is more free from personal jealousy and literary enmity than the Prussian philosopher. It may well be believed that he has not an enemy, and many are the warm friends whom his urbanity and warm generosity have attached to him. We shall have occasion to show in this article that he seems to feel more pleasure in claiming for others the reputation which he thinks they deserve than in demanding honour for himself. Nor is his influence confined to his own country. Domesticated equally in Paris as in Berlin, two of the chief European Academies regard him almost as an oracle; and in States with which he has no connexion, his influence has, to our own knowledge, been efficiently exerted, not merely for the promotion of science, by making suggestions for carrying on extended schemes of observation, but with two at least of the most jealous governments of Europe in procuring personal favours, and the relaxation of political decrees on behalf of persons engaged in scientific pursuits.[11]

The reviewers' opinions on Humboldt's impartiality are somewhat qualified at the end of the article:

But we have yet another remark which justice requires us to make without meaning at all to detract from the cordial expression of approba-tion which we have pronounced. Though our author disclaims the intention of deciding claims of priority in scientific discoveries, it would be quite impossible to avoid them in a work like the present. Now on questions of individual or of national claims, Baron Humboldt will be tried by a severer standard of impartiality than most writers. . . . Neither France nor Germany has any right to complain of the share which Humboldt has assigned to them in the great struggle for physical dis-covery. But we cannot rise from the careful perusal of this elaborate work without feeling that our own country has come off second, or rather *third* best. The physics have (it seems to us) been written for the longitude of Paris, and the geology for that of Berlin; and no one, we think, who is conversant with the scientific circles of those capitals, can fail to see that the selection of topics and of authors is tinged with the unconscious prejudices of local opinion.

In saying so much (and we could not feel ourselves justified in saying less) we are far from imputing to Baron Humboldt any motive less amiable than a desire to gratify distinguished contemporaries whom a less noble-minded person might have regarded rather with jealousy than with deference. To his ancient ally, von Buch, especially this deference seems to surpass what could reasonably be expected or wished. The whole of the geological and some other relative parts of the work are not merely filled with citations in flattering terms from the writings of the 'greatest geologist of our time' but whether in matters of fact or in great theories, in trivial or important coincidences of opinion, nay, even what is pointedly omitted or gently allowed to subside into neglect, the geo-logical reader traces so exact a transcript of the well-known and *stereo-typed* opinions of von Buch that he feels as if our author had forgotten his individuality of opinion in the anxious desire to applaud and flatter his friend. . . . If we recollect what has been done in England for modern geology—what is imperishably inscribed in the history of the science by its nomenclature—the members, deceased or alive, of the Geological Society of London might have reasonably expected to fill a more prominent place in the scientific history of the last forty years. . . . It is all well to signalise Hooke as having been the first to perceive the possibility of the chronological identification of strata by fossils but it cannot justify the defect of impartiality in the recent history. We have even remarked that throughout this volume our author is curious in his researches into the *early* history of English science—witness his allusion to Hooke—to Gilbert's proposal to determine latitude by magnetic dip—to Bacon on the form of continents—Childrey's first description of the zodiacal light— and Halley on the cosmical origin of aërolites; but this does not all console us—but the reverse—for the sparing allusions to the *great steps* made in Great Britain in the modern branches of science. . . . We miss the recognition of the place which our geologists are entitled to hold in the history of science which was never so conspicuous as within the recollection of those now alive.

We have alluded to geology in particular because the defect is striking, and because the subject is generally understood in this country. Perhaps in some other branches of science the deficiency is even more striking; but we do not choose to dwell upon a topic at once disagreeable and invidious; and we are very willing to conclude with an admission highly creditable to Baron Humboldt. We perceive no trace of personal illwill or jealousy in any part of the book or its citations. In the part where our author has allowed most scope to his unbiassed and best informed judgment, there it is most impartial and most comprehensive. Distinguished as a traveller, he might have had some temptation to withhold or attenuate the praises which our British scientific navigators and explorers have so peculiarly merited. But it is exactly the reverse: the praises of Burnes, of Darwin, of Franklin, Beechey and Ross are amongst the most cordial in the book. Where our author could draw most on his own stores of knowledge and was least subjected to the influence of less highminded friends, there his native generosity is best shown.[11]

Humboldt talked of the world of creation but never talked of God as his perturbed reviewers quickly pointed out:

He becomes involved and obscure and seems to feel his ground shake under him whenever his subject inevitably leads him for a moment from the detail of phenomena and classification to speak of, or hint at, the remotest idea of causation. . . . It is easy to say that the 'ultimate end of the experimental sciences is to ascend to the existence of laws, and to generalise them progressively'; but where is the inductive process to end? Where is the last generalisation of the last and highest group of laws? The contemplation of a law of nature derived from the generalisation of individual facts is as purely a subject of abstract intellectual conception as any founded on moral phenomena; and the reasoning through a chain of causes must evidently bring us at last to the first cause of all— be it Necessity or be it God.

We are far indeed from delighting in the tendencies of some authors on natural sciences to drag in religious views at every turn, thus secularising things sacred in the attempt to sanctify things profane. We conceive it to be impossible for any well-constituted mind to contemplate the sum and totality of creation, to generalise its principles, to mark the curious relations of its parts, and especially the subtle chain of connexion and unity between beings and events apparently the most remote in space, time and constitution without referring more or less to the doctrine of final causes and to the *design* of a superintending providence. We call it the highest pedantry of intellect to put to silence suggestions which arise spontaneously in every mind whether cultivated or not, when engaged in such contemplations; and we are sorry to observe in the work before us a silence on such topics as must attract the attention of at least every English reader.[11]

The time and the *Quarterly Review* were not attuned to agnosticism. Humboldt's attitude to religion can be summed up in his own words: 'All religions offer three different things, a moral rule, the same in all religions and very pure, a geological dream and a myth or legend; the last element has assumed the greatest importance.'

There is one important aspect of *Cosmos* which has been completely passed over by his reviewer, and that is the style, over which Humboldt had taken so much trouble. He had disciplined his tendency to overlong sentences where subjugate clause is fitted into subjugate clause, a tendency to which the German language lends itself so easily. There is nothing wooden or pedantic about his prose; its flowing elegance ensures for it a place in German literature.

VII. Photograph of Alexander von Humboldt (1857)

Fifteen

THE LAST YEARS

AT the outbreak of the February revolution in Paris, Arago, who had been a member of the chamber of deputies for some time, entered the provisional government; he remained politically active until the collapse of the revolutionary movement. Political demonstrations began to occur in the streets of Berlin by the beginning of March 1848; soon the first barricades appeared and the news of a successful revolt in Vienna drove the government to military measures. Troops held the royal palace; the King wanted to avoid any bloodshed; Prince William, the brother of the King and the future Emperor William I of Germany, a man of authoritarian character, demanded action against the mob. To begin with, the King gave in to the demands of the people and granted a constitution. The decree was published on the morning of the 18th of March, but the troops were not withdrawn, contrary to the advice of the Berlin municipal administration. The crowds collected again round the palace, and the troops were ordered to clear the streets. Two shots fell, and with the cry 'Traitors', the street battle, barricades and all, began in earnest. By midnight, the military, victorious, held and barred the surroundings of the palace. On the next day, the troops were withdrawn at the insistence of the King or more probably that of his minister; the infuriated commanding general permitted them to leave the town since the Berliners vented all their verbal aggressiveness on them. In their innocence, they thought that the revolution had succeeded; their fury turned against Prince William who was popularly supposed, and not without reason, to have been responsible for the military action. He escaped, in disguise,

to London, where he was soon to be joined by that main insti'
gator of political reaction, Metternich. The dead revolutionaries
were carried through the streets of Berlin in a solemn procession,
with the elderly Humboldt among the men in the lead, and
watched from the balcony of the palace by the King and the
Queen, more under duress than from their own free will. More
concessions followed; a liberal government was formed, and a
national assembly elected. Every citizen of the country had the
right to vote, and voting was secret. The new assembly met on
the 22nd of May with the chief task to formulate the constitu'
tion; it consisted in the majority of members of the professional
classes and civil servants; the farmers and artisans were well
represented. Only the industrialists and the owners of the large
estates had kept out of it. Surprisingly enough, Prince William
of Prussia, whose exile had not been of long duration, had had
himself elected in the honest intention, as he declared later in
his life, to take part in the creation of the constitution, pre'
sumably to exert a restraining influence on too liberal measures.
At the same time, a general German assembly met in Frank'
furt to prepare the ground for a unified German state. During
the summer, the big land owners, the 'Junkers', had rallied;
incensed by the proposals of the Prussian assembly to free the
tenant farmers from all personal services and to impose direct
taxes on the landed aristocracy, they formed a union for the
protection of property, meaning their own, and together with
the higher clergy and the conservative'minded members of the
administration, the nucleus of a conservative party was formed;
it soon re'established its influence in court circles. The new
constitution, which tried to found a parliamentarian govern'
ment in Prussia, was indignantly repudiated by the King.
Meanwhile, Austrian troops had appeared at the gates of
Vienna, where the revolutionaries were still holding out, and
the Prussian assembly demanded that the Prussian government
should support the popular movement in Austria with all
possible means. The petition did not find a majority and new

demonstrations in the streets followed. The cabinet resigned and the King seized the opportunity to force a conservative government on the assembly. To the proposal to nominate Bismarck, he replied that he would only do it when bayonets reigned unrestrained, and chose instead a general who had shown himself slightly less ruthless. When the assembly pro-tested, it was adjourned and forced to sit in the small provincial town of Brandenburg to sever its connexion with the people of Berlin. The militia which had been formed after the with-drawal of the troops, was dissolved and a state of siege declared in the capital and its environs. By the end of the year, the assembly was no more; a constitution was enforced by royal decree. The revolution was over; only a much more bloody conflict could have produced a different result in view of the intransigent mentality of the aristocracy who were not averse from bloodshed and the phantasies of a king who sincerely believed in the existence of a mystical union between him and his people.

Humboldt's attitude to these events can only be inferred. All traces of too great an enthusiasm for the 'magic movement' as Arago called it, have been carefully erased from the records of history. It is authenticated that he was one of the leaders in the funeral procession of the 'March victims'. He is also known to have joined the union of the artisans, a rudimentary trade union which had been formed in the early days, a fact which is even today only grudgingly admitted. There remain his letters. Thus he writes at the end of May to French friends that he is occu-pied with much more important things than with his work on *Cosmos*. Much more illuminating is a letter to Arago, written from Sans-Souci on the 16th of May 1848, which does not leave many doubts:

My ardent hopes for democratic institutions, hopes which date back to 1789, have been fulfilled. In the bloodstained night of the 18th of March, placed between two barricades, I was attacked four times by armed men, who did not know me and who had not read *Cosmos*, who wanted to search for arms. The groups did some damage by breaking down the doors. I talked to them of my white hair and the boring sentimental drama succeeded. We live at the moment in a state of anarchy supported by clubs which pretend to be more the expression of the will of the people than the assembly elected by universal suffrage. I do not complain of a state of affairs through which we must necessarily pass.

I continue to find much affection in the lower classes of society. I have taken part in the general election in the union of artisans but although I have been proposed as a candidate for Frankfurt, I have refused to accept anything. I shall be 80 next year, and in this fossilised state I cannot begin a new career.

Eighteen months later he writes: 'The year 1849 is the year of reaction. I have saluted 1789, I have been present at so many dramatic political events (monarchy, crowned republic) and now, at the age of eighty, I am reduced to the worn-out hope that the fine and ardent wish for free institutions is maintained in the people, that, periodically, it may appear to be asleep but that it is eternal as the electromagnetic storm which sparkles in the sun.'[1]

His relations to the royal family remained unchanged; the King and Queen attended the celebrations of his eightieth birthday at Tegel, now in possession of his brother's daughter Caroline, and he continued his service at court. The personal relationship between him and Frederick William seems to have been unimpaired although he had lost any influence over his actions. The reigning conservative and church circles, however, took a different view; Humboldt was placed under police surveillance. For some years, his house was watched and all his letters opened by the censor. 'I have become *persona non grata* in the last years and would have been exiled as a revolutionary and as the author of the godless *Cosmos* if my position with the king had not prevented it. I am an abomination to the pietists and the *Kreuzzeitung* (the new conservative paper); they would like nothing more than to have me moulder underground.'[2]

He continued with the life to which he had disciplined

himself and noticed with clinical detachment the symptoms of a very advanced age:

I lead a dreary and monotonous life in the middle of so much restlessness. I do not have to explain the reasons for my disgust and my mental discomfort. My health and my capacity for work are marvellously preserved in spite of the cold ($-20°$ F), and the eternal drives to Charlottenburg on duty. Only the hours of the night are undisturbed. I work usually from 9 until 3 o'clock. I very rarely go to bed before 3 o'clock in the morning, but I sleep longer than I used to, generally until 7 or 8 o'clock. I do not find at all that I feel better if I sleep eight or nine hours which would be quite possible because I can still sleep when I want to, even during the day. What I see myself lose, that is the sureness of muscular movements, I can stand for three or four hours without feeling the strain, but I do not feel really safe when I reach for books from a ladder, when I go down a very steep staircase, when I climb into a very high carriage.

I am publishing two books all at once, the third volume of *Cosmos* and a collection of new and old memoirs under the title of 'Geological and physical memoirs', in the pure German of Erfurt. Since the printing is done deep in the south (in Stuttgart), I have a lot of trouble and sometimes eight or ten proofsheets to correct at the same time.

It is all too necessary as I have had to give serious thought to some old debts. I have been able to pay £950 last year by this kind of work which was urgently demanded of me. These agitated times do not make for prosperous finances. The position becomes so much more delicate since I feel more than ever the necessity for the dignity of independence to maintain my individuality as a man now that the greater interests are suspended.[3]

The Micawberish state of his finances still harassed Humboldt; in fact, it survived him. It probably explains too why he did not resign from his official position until he was well into the eighties. His brother's children, who had inherited wealth and married wealth, were greatly puzzled at the 'uncle's' addiction to life at court and seem never to have given a thought to the accompanying regular income.

In Paris the new French republic collapsed in December

1851 with the *coup d'état*; Louis Napoleon was on the way to the throne. Arago was arrested with other opponents of Napoleon's ambitions. His life had been for some time a constant battle for his position at the observatory and against the reforms at the École Polytechnique where the predominantly theoretical teaching was to be reduced, partly under the pretext that it hindered practical technical training and partly from political reasons: a good knowledge of the calculus was suspect as an encouragement of socialistic leanings. His stay in prison was short but he did not survive for very long.

Humboldt reacted to the new outrage to his political feelings with all his vigour. 'Louis Napoleon's usurpation reminds me more of the chronicles of the tyrants of ancient Greece or medieval Italy than of the generals of the Roman empire. They were raised to the throne mainly by military fame and crude force; here, however, a predominant element of trickery comes to the aid of force. A whole system of fraudulent ideas is propagated as a complete creed and brilliant programmes of promises and reforms are intended to deceive the people over the loss of their freedom. This state of affairs makes me doubly sad when I look at the sophistical adventurers, speculators and ambiguous characters of every kind who push to the front of the nation, when I see the fatalism, the servility in the mass of the French people which only further the plans of the usurper.'[4] And Varnhagen reports: 'Humboldt came at one o'clock. He is furious about the *coup d'état* in France, about the force, the arbitrary banishments. The King was at first jubilant, neither he nor the court objected to the shameful action against the people, the assembly, against justice and solemn oaths but now that the adventurer keeps the universal suffrage, appeals to the people, practises socialism and wants to become emperor, now they hate him. Humboldt says that Louis Bonaparte is indubitably the son of Admiral Verhuel, his brother Morny a son of General Flahault, who lived with both sisters, the Queen of Holland and the Queen of Naples.'[5]

When Arago became dangerously ill, political scruples made it impossible for Humboldt to hurry to Paris. 'I would at once take the train but I am held back less by fear for the health of my 81 years than by a moral and political principle as you may have guessed. My position, so close to the king, makes it impossible for me, however small my personal importance may be, to come to Paris without going to the Élysée. It would be assumed that the king does not permit it. To pay my respects to the president and Mme. Demidoff at this moment would cost me too much of my integrity. You know the colour of my opinions which have not varied since 1789; I can come to terms with the republic in which I have lived although I find it no less artificial than the so-called constitutional monarchy but I cannot come to terms at all with a hereditary republic, with an imperial restitution.'[6] There are hints that in the end, when Arago's state was evidently hopeless, Humboldt was not allowed to go: 'Not a human gesture from "above". No sign of interest, I want to say no spontaneous movement to make it possible for a brother to take a dying man in his arms.'[7]

Arago died in October 1853 and with him the ties with France. Humboldt, nearly twenty years older, survived him until 1859, working away without much happiness, harassed by visitors and correspondents, begging letters and cranky ladies trying to convert him, harassed so much that two months before his death he wrote a pathetic letter to the papers, imploring his tormentors to reduce their correspondence with a man to whom so little time was left. He was still honoured by the scientific world; in 1852, the Royal Society awarded him the Copley medal for his work in the field of geophysics. He did not himself go to London; the medal was handed by Lord Rosse, the president, to Bunsen, the Prussian envoy, with the address:

Chevalier Bunsen, I am most happy to have the honour of committing to your care the Copley medal for Baron Humboldt. The Royal Society have awarded him the highest honour which it was in their power to confer, to mark their sense of the great value of his contributions to Terrestrial Physics during a long series of years. Your Foreign Secretary has recently drawn up for the Council an account of Baron Humboldt's researches: that has been printed, and therefore it will be unnecessary for me to go over the same ground again. It is enough to say that there is no one acquainted with the present state of magnetism, of zoology, of botany, of geology, or of physical geography who is not aware of the extent and value of Baron Humboldt's researches. A scientific traveller of the highest order, he zealously endeavoured to advance the science of physical geography in its widest sense, regardless of toil and expense, and at great personal risk. Distant regions of the globe were in turn his habitation, and with remarkable patience and a sagacity peculiarly his own, he sought out Nature's laws under every modification of climate. The mass of facts which he has given to the world, carefully arranged and discussed, constitute a mine of information from which cosmogonists will long continue to draw with profit while in its vastness it will be regarded with astonishment as the work of one man.[8]

In a rather fulsome reply, Bunsen expressed his gratification: 'The most ancient and illustrious institution of Europe has awarded its highest honour to the Nestor and prince of the men of science of my country. . . . But you have honoured more in Humboldt—you have honoured humanity; for Humboldt ever has been a true cosmopolite as well as a good patriot; he has ever been a friend of mankind.'[8]

Humboldt's fight for the abolition of slavery had a sequel during the struggle between Fremont and Buchanan for the presidency of the United States in 1856. A new translation of the original Spanish version of the *Political Essay* had been printed in New York in which the entire chapter on the political and economic position of the Mexican slaves had been suppressed. Humboldt immediately published a statement in a liberal paper in Berlin in which he expressed his objections to the dismemberment of his book. The omitted part had for him greater importance than all the geographical and statistical data. The article was reprinted in American newspapers with an encouraging effect on the election propaganda of the Republican party. Fremont wrote to Humboldt: 'In the history of your life and opinions we find abundant reasons for believing that in the struggle in which the friends to liberal progress in this country find themselves engaged, we shall have with us the strength of your name.'⁹ The abolitionists even tried to make capital out of Humboldt's recognition of Fremont's scientific achievements, surely the first and only time that scientific prestige was turned to political ends. Buchanan won the election; Humboldt's reputation did not have quite enough weight against the mainly economic forces on the other side. There was one, slightly derisory consequence, a change in Prussian legislation which, until then, had conceded to foreigners staying in the country the right to retain their slaves. Every negro was from then on to become free as soon as he touched Prussian soil, which would presumably have included Prussian ships in foreign harbours. Humboldt, however, saw in this law a personal achievement for which he had struggled for a long time.

In the autumn of 1857, the reign of Frederick William IV came to an end with the complete mental collapse of the King. When it became evident in the following year that he would not recover, his brother took up the reins as Prince Regent; the scene was now set for Bismarck and the founding of the German empire under Prussian leadership. Humboldt withdrew into private life; he had already left the privy council four years earlier for reasons which had nothing to do with old age but everything with the new masters. His position at court had had its unpleasant moments in the last years. To the young men he appeared as the old bore who talked too much, and the King and his contemporaries had heard it all before. For over twenty years, Humboldt had had the task, partly perhaps self-imposed, of reading aloud in the evenings; with his pedagogical bent, he chose biographies of scientists and scholars or newspaper articles of a liberal tendency. But lately he had been superseded by a young actor, a favourite of the King, who recited poetry or read the latest novels. Humboldt battled on and tried to break in as soon as his rival stopped to take a breath. At one such occasion when he had been reduced to complete silence, he sought solace in food, as Bismarck has reported. He heaped his plate with *foie gras*, smoked eel, lobster, and other indigestibles and ate morosely. Soon after, he left—if we can believe the story of Bismarck, who was astounded at the old man's healthy appetite. The future chancellor listened or at least pretended to listen when Humboldt talked and thought he was quite liked by him. It is a fact, however, that his name is never mentioned in Humboldt's letters or in his conversations with Varnhagen. It seems incredible that he should not have noticed Bismarck's calibre, if only as a reactionary of the kind he most detested. His political judgement was in many cases remarkably far-sighted, as in the words he wrote during the French campaign for the conquest of Algiers: 'The importance attached by a feeling of national honour to the possession of Algiers—a wretched colony, yielding only corn and oil— exerts a baneful influence on the military. Algiers tends to infuse a spirit of ferocity into the army and demoralises the nation by the way in which the governors have been allowed to deceive and oppress the people.'[10]

Humboldt had a slight stroke in 1857 which did not leave any permanent damage, and on the 6th of May 1859, he died a truly natural death after a fortnight of increasing weakness. His grateful country gave him a state burial in the cathedral of Berlin with all pomp and circumstance. He is interred in the family vault in Tegel where direct descendants of Wilhelm Humboldt are still in residence. At the burial service it was hinted that Humboldt's attitude to orthodox faith was somewhat doubtful, as he had always observed a 'shy silence' on this question; in Lord Houghton's phrase, he had been a tranquil unreligionist. In contrast to his brother, he had not believed that, after death, we shall learn more about the eternal order of the universe. 'With little suspense and expectation, one likes to be pleasantly surprised.'[11]

The testamentary dispositions of Humboldt became a public scandal before the funeral was over, to the delight of the Ber-liners who have always taken a malicious pleasure in the human weaknesses of the great. For the last ten years of his life, his domestic peace had been very much in the hands and at the mercy of his old and on the whole faithful servant Seifert. It was Seifert who regulated the admission of visitors for a con-sideration and who indicated that the guest had better go. For over thirty years he had, together with his wife, looked after his master, kept house for him and accompanied him on his travels, for the then quite normal wage of £45 a year. In the moments of financial crisis he had, quite voluntarily, forgone his payments until the situation improved again. Humboldt, who felt the obligation to provide for Seifert, had made a testament in 1841 in which he left all his personal possessions to his servant and had confirmed his dispositions in a letter to his valet on the 13th of March 1855: 'My dear Seifert, To prevent any kind of slander about your honourable and honest character, I confirm by this letter (because, at my advanced age, I could be over-taken by death suddenly) that I have given to you and your heirs, in my lifetime and of my own free will, as a reward for your care and attention the sum of £415 (the value of the decoration of the order of the Red Eagle, first class, in diamonds, paid out to me with great liberality by the ministry of the royal house on my appeal in February 1855). I repeat here what I have deposed in my testament of the 10th of May 1841, that I leave to you and after your death to your heirs all my personal possessions such as: gold medals, chronometers and clocks, books, maps, paintings, engravings, sculptures, instruments, my sable coat, linen, the small amount of plate, beds, furniture, with the to me painful request to reduce my debt by the sale of the "Chalcography" which alone is worth more than £385 in the case that the king who has been so generous just lately, could not accede to my petition for the gift of a few hundred pounds to pay my debts with the bank of A. Mendelssohn which has been so helpful in the last fifty years. Your honourable mind and your respect for my reputation will make this a pleasant duty. My continued nightly labours will perhaps enable me to pay my entire debts before my not far distant decease.'[12] The King, who had several times helped Humboldt in his lifetime with larger sums of money, settled his overdraft, a matter of £200, after his death. A few months before, Humboldt had transferred by a deed of gift all his property to his servant, retaining its use for as long as he was alive. Expressly excepted were only the diaries and manuscripts, the royal cabinet orders, the Copley medal, a portrait of Frederick William IV, and a vase with pictures of the royal palaces in SansSouci and Charlottenburg.

While the dead body of Humboldt was still lying in state in his library, Seifert asserted his rights as the owner in the face of the officials who had come to seal the contents of the flat, in compliance with the usage of the country. The family was horrified at the 'incredible will of the poor dear uncle': 'It is all very sad and quite incomprehensible, and more painful than anything else is the thought that the uncle has been in such unworthy hands as becomes more and more apparent, and it is so sad and distressing that everything is public property already.'[13] The *Kreuzzeitung*, Humboldt's old enemy, had been the first with the news. The family was equally displeased with the obituary in the liberal paper which had made too much, for their liking, of the dead uncle's political leanings. An attempt was made by Seifert to interest the Prince Regent in the acquisition of Humboldt's library; after a valuation of the contents, the minister of education, however, did not feel prepared to recommend the purchase. The entire collection, comprising over 11,000 volumes, was sold to a Berlin bookseller who handed them on to an American firm in London. The books were finally put into the hands of Sotheby's and perished there in a fire. The stir made by the affair was not so easily for-gotten, although the details became blurred; the *Encyclopaedia Brittanica* describes it in the discreet sentences: 'In his later years, the somewhat arbitrary sway of an old and faithful servant held him in more than matrimonial bondage. By a singular example of weakness, he executed, four years before his death, a deed of gift transferring to his man Seifert the absolute possession of his entire property. It is right to add that no undue ad-vantage appears to have been taken of this extraordinary concession.'[14]

Varnhagen had preceded his old friend in death by a few months; he had left all his papers and his collection of letters and autographs to his niece Ludmilla Assing, who had kept house for him after the decease of his wife. She lost no time in preparing his correspondence with Humboldt for publica-tion, and the letters together with extracts from Varnhagen's diaries burst on the scandalized public in the spring of 1860. The editress had felt authorized by some lines in one of Hum-boldt's letters: 'Your last and very flattering letter contains some words which I should not like to misinterpret. "You grudge yourself the possession of my impieties." You may dispose of such possessions as you wish after my not too distant death.'[15] The correspondence was printed without any altera-tions or elisions: 'In fulfilling so sacred a duty, it was an act of piety to leave every word exactly as it was written. To have presumed to alter his expressions would indeed have been an insult to the memory of Humboldt.' A number of people who had been the target of Humboldt's malicious remarks which were so faithfully recorded in the diary, were not particularly pleased, and public conventions were outraged by Hum-boldt's discontent with life at court. The English edition of the book was an equal shock to public opinion in this country, so much so that Lord Houghton who had been a friend of Varn-hagen's and who had met Humboldt on his visits to Berlin, felt impelled to publish a vindication of his attitude, a vindication based on his personal experience of the Prussian court in the years 1845 to 1846:

The position of Humboldt at that period was the cause of sincere gratification to all those who loved to see genius successful and rewarded, and also the source of much envy on the part of all whose merits had never been acknowledged, either by prince or people, as they thought was deserved. His intellectual eminence indeed was so unchallenged that when he passed from writing a chapter of *Cosmos* to his daily reserved place at the royal table opposite the king, there was no pretence either of favouritism or of service—it was the fair and honourable inter-change of the highest social station and the noblest mental powers; the patronage was on both sides. Who suspected the deep discontent that lay at the bottom of that old man's heart? Who believed that he was seeking refuge from that courtly splendour, and even from that royal friendship, in secret satire and confidential depreciation of all about him poured into the ear of a literary contemporary of whose complete sympathy he was well assured?

It will astonish many to read the specimens of the intimate corre-spondence between prince Metternich and a man whose political opinions he must have regarded as dangerous and detestable but whose knowledge he could reverence, and of whose friendship he was proud.

With the reign of Frederick William IV came a mode of thought and an estimate of men and things to which it was difficult, if not impossible, for the great minds which had battled through the glories and the ruins of the French Revolution to do justice. M. de Talleyrand used to say that only those who had lived near the conclusion of the last century could realise the worth of the world to man; and we can fairly test the depth of those impressions by their endurance to the very last in the nobler spirits that had traversed the whole round of disappointment, and to whom all faith might well seem to be illusory and vain.

Humboldt himself could not have been an active and earnest poli-tician. The largeness of his views, derived from such long and accurate observations of nature and of man, must have induced that indifference to the immediate contingencies of human affairs which is at once the penalty and the consolation of the highest and fullest minds. . . . It was by this abstinence that he probably retained an influence which he could frequently exercise to mitigate the severity of cases of individual oppression and sometimes to sustain the really noble and imaginative spirit of his royal master above the sordid policy of expediency and fear.

He was but too conscious that he was looked upon by the society in which he lived as a sort of moral Helot—a sad example of what a man might come to when drunk with knowledge. No amount of diplomatic reserve could have made him acceptable to his fellow-courtiers, and it was only as a link between the intellectual qualities of the sovereign and the literature and science of the nation that he could feel himself in any legitimate vocation. In the various and remarkable creations of art which have elaborately decorated the least lively of cities—in the great geo-graphical and antiquarian explorations which Prussia has of late years undertaken, some of them in connection with English enterprise—in the composition and production of costly works of national or general interest—in the judicious and delicate relief of destitute men of letters, the authority of Humboldt was continuously and powerfully exercised without a suspicion of favouritism or partiality.

Apart from these useful and honourable functions, the question may well be asked whether the connection of Baron Humboldt with the court of Prussia was one which can be regarded with satisfaction rela-tively to the dignity of literature and the worth of the human mind? And yet, if not this, what position of any man of genius or the highest erudi-tion in the constant intimacy of any court is desirable or even tenable? Enjoying the entire esteem and real friendship of two sovereigns, Hum-boldt remains as unindulgent to the princely character as if he were an outer democrat, and falls foul even of our amiable and intellectual Prince Consort who approached him with a cordial admiration which would have been very acceptable to any English man of letters. What philosopher at court can be expected to keep his judgment clear and his temper cool where the wise and kindly Humboldt so failed?

The wide gulf which in our country separates the men of thought from the men of action is assuredly no small evil. In its effect on the poli-tical and social character of the upper ranks it maintains a low standard of mental labour, content with official aptitude, with adroit representa-tion and facility of speech, and disparages the exercise of those spon-taneous and constructive faculties which should also give a man the command of his fellows in a reflective age; it encourages the consumption of a large portion of life in amusements which become occupations, serious frivolities only differing from vices as barren ground from weeds, and really perilous to the moral peace of the community by contrasting the continuous task of the working thousand with the incessant pleasure of the selected few. On the other hand, the isolation of the literary class has not only deformed some of our highest works of fiction by caricatures of manners and motives with which the writers have not been sufficiently familiar but has also engendered a sense of injustice which shows itself in wrong susceptibilities, in idle vaunts, in uncharitable interpretations and in angry irony. These painful feelings may rather increase than diminish with the practical equality that is advancing upon us with such rapid strides (but which the literary class are so often unwilling themselves to concede to others), and the imagined barrier may be all the more formidable when it ceases to rest on the palpable inequalities of fortune and the real dissimilarity of daily existence.

So noble indeed was the nature of Alexander von Humboldt that it preserved, under an almost life-long weight of patronage, the elevation of his intellect and the integrity of his heart. His indefatigable industry was unimpeded by the constant round of small duties and vapid amusements, and the luxurious security of his official position never blunted his eager interest in the new acquisitions of all science and in the fresh developments of literature. It was thus his signal good fortune to retain to the last not only the wonderful stores of knowledge accumulated through so many years but also the art to reproduce and dispose them for the delight and edification of mankind.

No advantage, however great, should be purchased at so costly a price as the sacrifice of that which is the only sure sign of the progress of nations and the very core of civilisation itself—the combination of moral strength with intellectual culture. There is thus something satisfactory in Humboldt's very dissatisfaction, in his criticism of the great, in his consciousness of an incomplete and jarring existence, in his struggle to escape from a conventional world to the confidences of a genial and undoubted friendship.[16]

Sixteen

ACHIEVEMENTS

GREAT and secure as Humboldt's reputation had been in his lifetime, it lost some of its lustre after his death. Once his authority had gone and with it his usefulness, those people who had always thought his influence excessive, now criticized him openly. Only ten years later, it had become the fashion to find his work shallow and to dwell with gusto on his errors which new developments had made manifest. It was a decade of revo/ lutionary progress in the sciences; beginning with Darwin's theory of the mechanism of natural evolution and the intro/ duction of spectral analysis by Kirchhoff and Bunsen, it saw the opening of a transformed medicine which resulted from the practice of asepsis. Maxwell published his electromagnetic theory and Mendeleef the periodic table of the chemical ele/ ments. Weather forecasting began in earnest, and the petroleum industry got into its stride. The typewriter was invented, the Suez canal was built and the chemical industry founded. The mainly empirical achievements of the first half of the century had now been given a firm mathematical basis and general laws extracted from the accumulated mass of data. The power of science began to appear limitless, and its godlike creators looked with amused condescension upon the ignorant efforts of their predecessors. They were too near to them to recognize how much they owed to their patient investigations and acute observations.

The methods of Humboldt's attack on scientific problems were in his lifetime already so widely disseminated that people were no longer aware of their origin. He is best remembered as an explorer—oh yes, the Humboldt current—whose deter/ minations of geographical latitudes and longitudes in South America were for over seventy years the basis for our know/ ledge of that region. He was much more than that; he laid the foundations of modern physical geography. The way in which he assembled all the factors which decide the geo/ graphical character of a country, climate, elevation above sea level, distribution of plants and animals and natural mineral resources became a model together with his treatment of the economics of a country as integral part of the geography. In geology, he opened a new chapter by his views on the im/ portance of eruptive processes as separate from sedimentation and on the alignment of volcanoes along subterranean fissures which were a completely new conception.

He is the founder of systematic meteorology and the geo/ graphy of plants. In both fields, his insistence on the necessity for accurate determinations of numerical data and his own example of the proper methods for their collection laid down the rules for future generations. It was the comparison of mean annual temperatures with the distribution of plant families which gave him the idea for the isothermal lines; he accom/ panied them with a discussion of the relative proportions in which the genera of plants appear at different geographical lati/ tudes and at different altitudes above sea level. It was the first picture of the dependence of vegetable life on climate which was based on numerical data.

Humboldt was started on his geomagnetic studies by Borda and has, in his own account, been scrupulously just. He had the good fortune to come back alive from South America and lay the results of his magnetic measurements before the scientific public. It is true that, sooner or later, some explorer would have observed the geomagnetic intensity in various geographical latitudes, but the timing might have been wrong and the com/ bination of the available material of figures and the mathe/ matical genius of Gauss might no longer have existed. In his

persistence on the observations of the regular and irregular perturbations of the geomagnetic field, Humboldt showed real
intuition, far in advance of his time.

The initiative he took in the organization of international
scientific collaboration has been of the greatest consequence for
the advance of our knowledge of geophysics and of the meteorological laws which form the basis of weather forecasting. The
institution of international geophysical years is directly descended from Humboldt's efforts.

Outside his purely scientific achievements, Humboldt has
been the first man to recognize the Inca and Aztec civilizations
as civilizations in their own right, the first man to give a
serious account of their religious traditions as a contribution to
the study of comparative religion and not as a tale of heathenish
practices. He showed even greater originality in seeing in
Aztec monuments the manifestations of an artistic achievement
which is still not universally granted to them.

Humboldt wrote not very long before his death an assessment of his own work: 'I have never been able to hoodwink
myself as I have always been surrounded by people who were
superior to me. My life has been useful to science less through
the little I have contributed myself than through my efforts to
let others profit of the advantages of my position. I have always
had a just appreciation of the merits of others, I have even
shown some acumen in the discovery of new talent. I like to
think that, while I was at fault to tackle from intellectual curiosity too great a variety of scientific interests, I have left on my
route some trace of my passing.' It is certainly true that he has
exerted a great influence through the help he gave to other
scientists, and by no means only to scientists, who would otherwise not have been able to continue their work.

He was a superb observer and a far-reaching innovator in the
organization of collecting numerical data, especially in fields
such as meteorology and geomagnetism where reliable results
follow only from a systematic accumulation of observations

extended over large areas and long periods of time, where, in short, mean values are needed whose importance he has stressed again and again. He was equally far-seeing in his choice of representation; his isothermal and isodynamic lines and his general predilection for the graphical method initiated the general use of this, now indispensable, procedure.

Humboldt was not the man to formulate a mathematically expressed general law out of a mass of numerical data; he rather threw off generalizations which pointed the way to further research. There is a certain anonymity attached to an influence of this kind, the anonymity of a great teacher.

BIBLIOGRAPHY

Friedrich Althaus, *Briefwechsel und Gespräche Alexander von Humboldt's mit einem jungen Freunde. Aus den Jahren 1848 bis 1856,* Berlin, 1861.

Louis Agassiz, *His life and correspondence,* edited by Elizabeth Cary Agassiz, in 2 vols., London, 1885.

François Arago, *Histoire de ma jeunesse, Oeuvres de François Arago, Notices Biographiques,* vol. 1, Paris, 1854.

Ewald Banse, *Alexander von Humboldt, Erschliesser einer neuen Welt. Grosse Naturforscher,* Band 14, Stuttgart, 1953.

Hanno Beck, *Gespräche Alexander von Humboldt's,* Berlin, 1959.

Alexander von Humboldt, vol. 1, Wiesbaden, 1959.

vol. II, Wiesbaden, 1961.

Karl Bruhns, *Alexander von Humboldt, Eine wissenchaftliche Biographie,* 3 vols., Leipzig, 1872.

Sir Charles Darwin, *Life and letters of Charles Darwin, including an auto-biographical chapter.* Edited by his son Francis Darwin in 3 vols., London, 1887.

A. Dove, *Die Forsters und die Humboldts. Zwei Paar bunter Lebensläufe zur allgemeinen deutschen Biographie beigetragen,* Leipzig, 1881.

François Gérard, *Correspondance de François Gérard, peintre d'histoire, avec les artistes et les personnages célèbres de son temps,* Paris, 1867.

C. F. Gauss, *Briefe zwischen Alexander von Humboldt und Gauss, heraus-gegeben von K. Bruhns,* Leipzig, 1877.

Sebastian Hensel, *Die Familie Mendelssohn,* Leipzig, 1929.

Albert Herrmann, *Lou-lan, China, Indien und Rom im Lichte der Ausgra-bungen am Lobnor,* Leipzig, 1931.

Alexander Herzen, *Erinnerungen,* Berlin, 1907.

C. F. Holder, *Louis Agassiz, His life and work,* New York and London, 1893.

J. D. Hooker, *Life and Letters of Sir John Dalton Hooker, O.M., G.C.S.T.,* based on material collected and arranged by Lady Hooker, by Leonard Huxley, 2 vols., London, 1918.

Therese Huber, geborne Heine, *Johann Georg Forsters Briefwechsel, nebst einigen Nachrichten von seinem Leben*, 2 vols., Leipzig, 1829.

Alexander von Humboldt, *Ideen zu einer Geographie der Pflanzen mit Naturgemälde der Tropenlender*, Stuttgart und Augsburg, 1805.

Ansichten der Natur mit wissenschaftlichen Erläuterungen, Stuttgart und Augsburg, 1808.

Vues des Cordillères et monuments des peuples indigènes de l'Amérique, Paris, 1810.

Essai politique sur le Royaume de la Nouvelle Espagne, Paris, 1811.

Voyage aux régions équinoxiales du nouveau continent fait dans les années 1799 à 1804 par Alexandre de Humboldt et Aimé Bonpland: Relations historiques, 3 vols., Paris, 1814–19.

Personal narrative of travels to the equinoxial regions of the new continent during the years 1799–1804. Translated by Helen Maria Williams, 5 vols., London, 1825.

Schwankungen der Goldproduktion, Deutsche Vierteljahresschrift, H4, Berlin, 1838.

The fluctuations of gold. Translated into English, revised and annotated by William Mandel, New York, 1900.

Lettre à Son Altesse Royale le Duc de Sussex, Président de la Royal Society de Londres, sur les moyens propres à perfectionner la connaissance du magnétisme terrestre par l'établissement de stations magnétiques et d'observations correspondantes, Proc. Roy. Soc. 3, 418, 1836.

Examen critique de l'histoire de la géographie du Nouveau Continent et des progrès de l'astronomie nautique aux 15e et 16e siècles, 6 vols., Paris, 1814–34.

Asie Centrale, recherches sur les chaînes de montagnes et la climatologie comparée, 3 vols., Paris, 1843.

Kosmos, Stuttgart, 1845–62, 5 vols.

Briefe an Varnhagen von Ense aus den Jahren 1827–58, Leipzig, 1860.

Briefwechsel mit Berghaus, 3 vols., Leipzig, 1863.

Humboldt und Cancrin, *Im Ural und Altai: Briefwechsel zwischen Alexander von Humboldt und Graf Georg von Cancrin*, Leipzig, 1869.

Alexander von Humboldt, *Briefe an seinen Bruder. Herausgegeben von der Familie von Humboldt in Ottmachau*, Stuttgart, 1880.

Lettres Américaines d'Alexandre de Humboldt, (1798–1807), Paris, 1905.

Correspondance d'Alexandre de Humboldt avec François Arago, (1809–1853), Paris, 1907.

BIBLIOGRAPHY

The Earl of Ilchester, *Chronicles of Holland House, 1820–1900*, London, 1937.

Professor Klencke, *Alexander von Humboldt: A biographical monument.* (Translated by Julietta Bauer), London, 1852.

Rudolf Lehmann, *An artist's reminiscences*, London, 1894.

Richard Monckton Milnes, Lord Houghton, *Monographs, personal and social*, London, 1873.

de la Roquette, *Oeuvres d'Alexandre de Humboldt, correspondance inédite scientifique et littéraire*, Paris, 1869.

Gustav Rose, *Mineralogisch-geognostische Reise nach dem Ural, dem Altai und dem Kaspischen Meer*, 2 vols., Berlin, 1837–42.

F. A. Schwarzenberg, *Alexander von Humboldt, or what may be accomplished in a life time*, London, 1866.

Anna von Sydow, *Gabriele von Bülow*, Berlin, 1926.

John Taylor, *Statements respecting the profits of mining considered in relation to the prospects of mining in Mexico.* In a letter to Thomas Fowell Buxton, Esq., M.P., by John Taylor, London, 1825.

Selections from the works of the Baron de Humboldt, relating to the climate, inhabitants, productions, and mines of Mexico. With notes by John Taylor, London, 1824.

K. A. Varnhagen von Ense, *Tagebücher*, 6 vols., Leipzig, 1861.

REFERENCES

Chapter I: The Beginning

(1) Bruhns, vol. 1, p. 41.
(2) Bruhns, vol. 1, p. 42.
(3) Letter to Pictet, 3 January 1806 (La Roquette).
(4) Bruhns, vol. 1, p. 45.
(5) Humboldt, *Kosmos*, vol. 1, p. 72.

Chapter II: Early Career and New Aims

(1) *Correspondance avec Arago*, Paris, Friday, 1831.
(2) Letter to Freiesleben, Bruhns, vol. 1, p. 218.
(3) Letter to Willdenow, Bruhns, vol. 1, p. 229.
(4) Letter to Pictet, Bruhns, vol. 1, p. 226.

Chapter III: The Llanoes

(1) Bruhns, vol. 1, p. 259.
(2) Darwin, *Life and Letters*: letter to J. D. Hooker, Down, 10 February 1845.
(3) *Briefe an seinen Bruder*, Cumana, 16 July 1799.
(4) Letter to Baron de Zach, Cumana, 1 September 1799 (*Lettres Américaines*).
(5) *Personal Narrative*, vol. IV, p. 143.
(6) *Ansichten der Natur: Über die Steppen und Wüsten*, p. 1.

Chapter V: The Andes and Mexico

(1) *Vues des Cordillères*, p. 239. (*Volcans d'air de Turbaco*).
(2) *Briefe an seinen Bruder*, Lima, 25 November 1802.
(3) *Vues des Cordillères*, p. 242 (*Volcan de Jorullo*).
(4) Letter from Jefferson, Washington, 28 May 1804 (Bruhns, vol. 1, p. 335).
(5) Bruhns, vol. 1, appendix IV.

Chapter VI: The Geomagnetic Field and Magnetic Storms

(1) *Le voyage de Humboldt et Gay-Lussac en Italie* (1805), *Lettres Américaines*, appendix 7, p. 245.
(2) *Kosmos*, vol. 1, p. 432.
(3) *Lettres Américaines*, appendix 7, p. 247.
(4) Letter to M. A. Pictet, Berlin, 3 January 1806 (*Lettres Américaines*).
(5) *Correspondance de François Gérard*, Berlin, 12 February 1807.

REFERENCES

Chapter VII: Paris and Arago

(1) Letter to M. A. Pictet, Paris, 28 February 1808 (*Lettres Américaines*).
(2) *Briefe an seinen Bruder*, Paris, 19 August 1813.
(3) Ibid., Milan, 11 October 1822.
(4) *Lettres Américaines*, appendix 10, p. 303.
(5) *Correspondance avec Arago*, London, 30 April, 1827.

Chapter VIII: The American Publications

(1) Letter to M. A. Pictet, 24 January 1796 (La Roquette).
(2) *Quarterly Review*, 14, 397, 1815–16 (Sir John Barrow).
(3) Letter to Don Antonio Joseph Cavanillos, Mexico, 22 April 1803 (La Roquette).
(4) *Kosmos*, vol. 1, p. 349.
(5) *Correspondance avec Arago*, Saarbrücken, 21 February 1843.
(6) *Quarterly Review*, 18, 114, 1817–18.
(7) *Quarterly Review*, 15, 453, 1816.
(8) *Essai politique*, p. 103.
(9) *Briefwechsel mit Berghaus*, Paris, 20 December 1825.
(10) Taylor, *Statements respecting the profits of mining*, p. 49.
(11) *Quarterly Review*, 42, 334, 1830.

Chapter IX: Return to Berlin

(1) *Goethes Briefwechsel mit Zelter*, Berlin, 28 January 1828.
(2) *Correspondance avec Arago*, Potsdam, 29 June 1828.
(3) Ibid., 25 February 1829.
(4) Letter from Cancrin to Humboldt, St. Petersburg, 15 August 1827 (*Im Ural und Altai*).
(5) Ibid., Humboldt to Cancrin, Berlin, 19 November 1827.
(6) Ibid., *Bemerkungen zu dem Briefwechsel über die Platinmünze*, p. 143.
(7) Ibid., Humboldt to Cancrin, Berlin, 26 February 1828.
(8) Ibid., Humboldt to Cancrin, Berlin, 10 January 1829.

Chapter X: Expedition to Siberia

(1) *Briefe an seinen Bruder*, Narva, 29 April 1829.
(2) Ibid., Barnaul, 4 August 1829.
(3) Alexander Herzen, *Erinnerungen*, p. 68.
(4) Leibniz to Peter the Great, *Asie Centrale*, vol. 3, p. 469.
(5) *Correspondance avec Arago*, Berlin, 15 January 1830.
(6) Varnhagen, *Tagebücher*, July 1830.

Chapter XI: Central Asian Geography

(1) Laplace, *Mécanique Céleste*, tome V, livre 11, chap. I, p. 3.
(2) *Asie Centrale*, vol. 1, p. 185.

(3) Ibid., vol. 2, p. 40.
(4) Ibid., vol. 2, p. 47.
(5) Herrmann, *Lou-lan*, p. 107.
(6) Rose, *Im Ural und Altai*, vol. 1, p. 353.
(7) Ibid., vol. 1, p. 357.
(8) *Asie Centrale*, vol. 3, p. 5.
(9) Agassiz, *Etude sur les glaciers*, chap. 18, p. 315.
(10) Agassiz, *His Life and Correspondence*, vol. 1, p. 269, letter from Humboldt to Agassiz, Berlin, 2 December 1837.
(11) Ibid., p. 315, Berlin, 15 August 1840.
(12) Letter to Sir Roderick Murchison, Potsdam, 12 January 1841 (La Roquette).
13) Letter to Alexander de Turgenev, 1831 (La Roquette).

Chapter XII: Organization of International Scientific Collaboration

(1) Agassiz, *His Life and Correspondence*, vol. 1, p. 187, letter from Humboldt to Agassiz, Paris, 27 March 1832.
(2) *Briefe an Varnhagen*, Berlin, 3 August 1838.
(3) Letter to Boussingault, Paris, 31 August 1822 (La Roquette).
(4) *Correspondance avec Arago*, Tegel, 10 April 1835.
(5) Ibid., Potsdam, 28 December 1832.
(6) *Proc. Roy. Soc.*, *3*, 418, 1836.
(7) *Kosmos*, vol. 1, p. 428.
(8) *Quarterly Review*, 77, 180, 1845–6.
(9) Letter to Letronne, Berlin, 26 December 1837 (La Roquette).
(10) *Examen critique*, vol. 1, p. 1.
(11) Ibid., vol. 3, p. 261.
(12) Ibid., vol. 3, p. 306.
(13) *Fluctuations of Gold*, p. 40.

Chapter XIII: The Eighteen-forties

(1) Letter to Letronne, Berlin, 26 December 1837 (La Roquette).
(2) *Gespräche mit einem jungen Freunde*, p. 29, 23 December 1849.
(3) *Correspondance avec Arago*, Berlin, 19 February 1840.
(4) Ibid., Berlin, 16 April 1840.
(5) Letter to Gide, Sans-Souci, 3 June 1840.
(6) *Correspondance avec Arago*, Berlin, 31 December 1840.
(7) *Briefe an Varnhagen*, Letter from Arago to Humboldt, Paris, 12 March 1841.
(8) Varnhagen, *Tagebücher*, Berlin, 18 December 1841.
(9) Ibid., Berlin, 24 February 1842.
(10) *Correspondance avec Arago*, Sans-Souci, 31 May 1842.
(11) Hooker, *Life and Letters*, Paris, 2 February 1845.
(12) *Edinburgh Review*, 112, 213, 1860.

REFERENCES

Chapter XIV: Cosmos

(1) Letter to Pictet, 24 January 1796. (La Roquette).
(2) *Briefe an Varnhagen*, Berlin 27 O,ctober 1834.
(3) Preface to *Kosmos*, vol. 1, p. v.
(4) *Kosmos*, vol. 1, p. 18.
(5) Ibid., vol. 1, p. 36.
(6) Ibid., vol. 1, p. 210.
(7) *Edinburgh Review*, 87, 209, 1848.
(8) *Kosmos*, vol. 2, p. 5.
(9) Ibid., vol. 1, p. 397.
(10) *Edinburgh Review*, 87, 172, 1848 (Sir John Herschel).
(11) *Quarterly Review*, 77, 154, 1845–6.

Chapter XV: The Last Years

(1) *Correspondance avec Arago*, Potsdam, 9 November 1849.
(2) *Gespräche mit einem jungen Freunde*, p. 95, 5 August 1852.
(3) *Correspondance avec Arago*, Berlin, 11 February 1850.
(4) *Gespräche mit einem jungen Freunde*, p. 99, 5 August 1852.
(5) Varnhagen, *Tagebücher*, 29 January 1852.
(6) *Correspondance avec Arago*, Berlin, 25 February 1852.
(7) Ibid., Berlin, 18 September 1853.
(8) *Proc. Roy. Soc.*, 6, 240, 1852.
(9) Bruhns, vol. 2, p. 295.
(10) Ibid., vol. 2, p. 167 (letter to K. von Wolzogen, 6 May 1837).
(11) *Briefe an Varnhagen*, Berlin, 6 April 1842.
(12) Bruhns, vol. 2, p. 296.
(13) von Sydow, *Gabriele von Bülow*, p. 532.
(14) *Encyclopaedia Britannica*, article on Alexander von Humboldt, 11th edition, 1910.
(15) *Briefe an Varnhagen*, Berlin, 7 December 1841.
(16) Lord Houghton, *Monographs, personal and social: Alexander von Humboldt at the court of Berlin*.

INDEX

INDEX

PRINTED IN GREAT BRITAIN BY
WESTERN PRINTING SERVICES LTD., BRISTOL

RENEWALS 458-4574

DATE DUE

DEC 15			
MAY 13			
DEC 13			
GAYLORD			PRINTED IN U.S.A.